eight plays for young people

D0395210

Prairie Play Series 6

eight plays
for young people

Prairie Performance II
edited by

Joyce Doolittle

NeWest Press
Edmonton

Canadian Cataloguing in Publication Data

Main entry under title:
Eight plays for young people

(Prairie play series ; 6)
ISBN 0-920316-90-5 (bound). — ISBN 0-920316-88-3 (pbk.)
1. Children's plays, Canadian (English)*
I. Doolittle, Joyce, 1928-   II. Title:
Prairie performance II.   III. Series.
PS8315.5.P73E39 1984   jC812'.54'0809
PR9196.3.E39 1984   C84-091196-3

Number 6 in the Prairie Play Series,
Diane Bessai, series editor.

Credits
Cover and book design: Susan Colberg
Typesetting: June Charter
Printing and binding: Friesen Printers Limited

Financial Assistance
Alberta Culture
The Canada Council

NeWest Publishers Limited
Suite 204, 8631 - 109 Street
Edmonton, Alberta
Canada   T6G 1E8

▪ Contents

Introduction

Canada has only recently acquired a significant body of plays written specifically for young people. This emerging genre shares much with the more established field of children's literature but is unique in being designed primarily for performance. Each of the eight plays by prairie playwrights chosen for this anthology includes characters and themes which are classic in children's literature. Heroes and heroines are often orphans, like Tom Sawyer or Anne of Green Gables. If parents do exist, they are generally inoperative or ineffectual, as in Lewis Carroll's *Alice* books or James Barrie's *Peter Pan*. Some plays have two or three protagonists—friends or siblings—working together, without adults, to solve important problems, as do the children in Arthur Ransome's books or in the Narnia series by C.S. Lewis. A search for self-hood through a dangerous and challenging journey provides the plot structure for two plays, reminding us of ancient myths and hero tales and of modern fantasy like Tolkien's *The Hobbit* and *The Lord of the Rings*. It is a measure of the growing maturity of our theatre for young people that so many of the plays in this volume draw upon archetypal sources but speak with a distinctive voice. Twenty years ago, most plays for the young in Canada copied models from the United States and England; adaptations of folk or fairy tales were the predominant style. Ten years ago, history plays were particularly popular as Canadians continued to unearth the past in the effort to capture an elusive "identity." Adaptations and plays based upon historical incident are still with us—and welcome—but today it is the variety of styles and the individuality of approach which impresses the playgoer and reader.

Plays are written primarily to be performed and the demand for stageworthy scripts for young people has been two-fold: school performances and family or holiday entertainments. Both are represented in this collection, with some satisfying the needs of both; but of the two, scripts for the schools have been more numerous. The special demands of the schools tour: small casts, portability, limited technical resources and a prescribed length (usually the standard forty-five or fifty minute class period) have forced playwrights to make their effects efficiently and to search for striking theatrical metaphors through form, style, and design as well as with the more traditional tools of the theatre—plot, dialogue, and characterization.

Two scripts in which a journey is taken by the hero are *Tikta'liktak* by Brian Paisley and *Cornelius Dragon* by Jan Truss. Paisley's play uses an Inuit legend and draws upon Inuit arts traditions of storytelling and mask making. As first produced by Chinook Touring Theatre in 1982, it used only three actors: one to play the hero throughout and the other two to act as storytellers and to play all of the masked and puppet animal characters with whom Tikta'liktak must struggle in order to survive his ordeal on an ice floe upon his Arctic odyssey. Courage, resourcefulness, and empathy with the world of nature are qualities which save the hero from death. The playwright has chosen several elements to increase the theatricality of the performance. Rather than relying upon realistic sound effects to indicate moments of danger, such as the breaking up of the ice, the drums beat ominously. Animals appear as masked figures or as puppets. The stage setting, "a dome of white," was created in the original production with a parachute. Jan Truss's hero with the vexing name, Cornelius Dragon, also goes on a journey. But Cornelius is a contemporary prairie boy—a runaway immigrant child on the edge of an uncomfortable adolescence. Although the characters are all modern people we would recognize in real life, Jan Truss's play has as many fantasy and theatrical elements as Paisley's. They are merely different in kind. A minimum of four characters are required to perform the play: one actor to play the hero throughout and one other male and two females to take on numerous roles. The author planned the small cast for a professional production with a limited budget for salaries. However, in a workshop production in 1983 at The University of Calgary, eleven players were used. One ingenious way the author has found to create large crowds required in the school dance sequence is to have "balloon heads" mounted on sticks. This stage property is worked into the action of the play directly when the hero, in a fit of frustration and despair, pops the balloons. The character of the cowboy in Cornelius Dragon is haunting. He is an example of the dark side of the "outsider"—as is Phil, the new kid in *Vandal.* The mood of the cowboy scene in the Truss script is reminiscent of the desert scene in *Peer Gynt,* Ibsen's fantasy journey play. Human nature, rather than animals or the elements, constitute Cornelius's trials. As is often the case in children's literature and theatre, the adults portrayed are, in the main, unreliable. A large part of the appeal and value of the journey play is that the hero or heroine must find within him or herself, the courage to overcome life's vicissitudes and to make peace with one's own limitations and human frailty.

Conflicts within families figure prominently in several of the plays in this collection. Cornelius Dragon resents his European parents "being different." In *The Other Side of the Pole* both Willy and Sandy, the protagonists, have difficulties with their folks. Willy has an off-stage mother whose negative feelings and actions are nonetheless felt on stage. Sandy's problems with her dad spring from his own difficulties with *his* father. In *Vandal*, Phil's betrayal of his dad triggers the play's climactic scene. In *Doctor Barnardo's Pioneers*, the trio of orphans encounter some difficult foster homes. But the play predominately about families is Alf Silver's *More of a Family*. In a variation of the journey play, with a nod to "The Secret Life of Walter Mitty" by James Thurber, Silver has written a modern play with an old-fashioned ending and message. Amy, the heroine, feels that her single-parent home is not enough of a family and, like Cornelius Dragon, she runs away—borrowing her mother's suitcase. She fantasizes about various kinds of families and finds the reality of each disappointing. The audience is able to relish two sets of performances from the actors, who equally enjoy portraying both the idealized and the actual families. By the end of her trip, Amy has reached downright dangerous alternatives and finds, as in Maeterlinck's classic, *The Bluebird*, that happiness was right at home all the time. The various ways in which these heroes and heroines deal with ambivalent feelings about their families—or lack of them—show readers and audiences problems they will recognize and reveal satisfactory and inappropriate ways of coping with them.

There is music in many of these plays, but the one which is clearly a musical is the family Christmas fantasy, *The Other Side of the Pole* written by Marney Heatley, Stephen Heatley and Edward Connell. First produced in Red Deer and Edmonton by Theatre Network in 1982, the play was expanded to include "framing scenes" when it was revived for a provincial tour and a triumphant revival in 1983. In its revised form, the "play within a play" takes place in Santa's workshop at the North Pole and allows for spirited elfin high jinks between separate episodes of the story of the abolishment of Christmas in the town of Split Hoof. *The Other Side of the Pole* is an example of a full length play intended for families at holiday time. Our ambivalent emotions about Christmas—its pressures, commercialism, and glitz versus a genuine belief in the original roots of the holiday, both pagan and Christian—find expression in this affectionate affidavit to forgiveness, giving, and joy. It was inspired to create the "son of Santa" whose childhood in the middle of tinsel tensions turned him off Christmas. And in the creation of Willy, a retarded boy whose love of life outweighs his limitations, the authors have given us a compelling protagonist.

Two plays draw directly upon historical events: *Doctor Barnardo's Pioneers* by Rick McNair and *The Day Jake Made Her Rain* by W.O. Mitchell. Rick McNair's play is based upon the phenomenon of the "Barnardo Boys"—orphans (both boys and girls) who were taken off the streets of slums in England, put into orphanages in England and then sent to Canada to work for their "keep." This project, begun by Barnardo in 1885 for humanitarian reasons was, nonetheless, naive in expectation and often cruel in consequences. As a part of his research, McNair spoke to a senior citizen about his memories as one of the orphan children who, with his sister, was sent to Canada. McNair then used the senior citizen's story as "framing scenes" for his episodic script, beginning and ending the play with a spirited exchange of memories and teasing between the elderly brother and sister. One of the theatrical delights of the performance is to see the actors' transformations from old to young or from character to character as they move from the streets of London, to the ship that carries them across the ocean and to various foster homes. The most theatrical personification of adult authority figures occurs in *Doctor Barnardo's Pioneers* when a "double figure" costumed as one giant person shows graphically how grown-ups often appear to small people. *Doctor Barnardo's Pioneers* was performed in two Stage-Coach Players' seasons, 1978 and 1983. In the first production five actors, three men and two women, played all the parts. In 1982 a Calgary high school, Bishop Grandin, performed the play with a cast of twenty-four.

The Day Jake Made Her Rain is the quintessential prairie play—it has all the things we have grown to expect from the genre: the land, the depression, the small town, the hired hand, the rainmaker, and jokes about gophers. No play is more entitled to be *sui generis*. W.O. Mitchell's "Jake and the Kid" classics began as short stories in *Macleans* magazine, where the author was fiction editor in 1948. *The Day Jake Made Her Rain* appeared in the March 1, 1948 issue—with piquant poetic justice, the line drawings of Jake which illustrate the story look a lot like W.O. Mitchell today! The story's next reincarnation was episode three of the then new radio series, "Jake and the Kid" on Tuesday, July 11, 1950. In 1961, the novel *Jake and the Kid* included, as chapter 11, "The Day Jake Made Her Rain." Mitchell received the Leacock

Medal for Humor in 1962 for the Jake stories and radio shows. In the 1975-76 season of plays at Alberta Theatre Projects under the direction of Douglas Riske, *The Day Jake Made Her Rain* became a successful stage play. W.O. Mitchell says that the first staged version was an amateur production in the mid-fifties in Fort Qu'Appelle, Saskatchewan, produced in the theatre of the old court house by Florence and Burton James. The author claims there had been a long drought that year—and that it started to rain as the curtain fell. Such stories, whether apocryphal or genuine, illustrate the charm and strength of this piece. Besides capturing through Crocus, Saskatchewan and its inhabitants the essence of rural life during the thirties and forties, Mitchell has created a character in the hired man, Jake, who combines the Jungian trickster and wise old man with Bunyanesque tall tales. The friendship of the fatherless "kid" (played in the Alberta Theatre Projects production as a girl) and the old outsider, Jake, is believable and heart warming. The canny mixture of hoax and faith convinces all but the most cynical reader or playgoer that God is (this time) on our side. And the rainmaking machine—fun to create in one's own mind as a reader—becomes another actor in its Rube Goldberg glory on stage.

Melody and the Bag Lady by Rex Deverell and *Vandal* by William Horrocks are plays about social problems: vagrants and eccentrics and how to live with them, and suppressed rage and impotence erupting in violence and destruction. Outsiders appear in almost all of the plays in this book and include the cowboy in *Cornelius Dragon*, Ben in *More of a Family*, Willy in *The Other Side of the Pole*, another Willie in *Doctor Barnardo's Pioneers* and Jake in *The Day Jake Made Her Rain*—but it is in Rex Deverell's script that the outsider is identified as having a problem about which something "must be done." Melody, Sarah, and Ivan are friends and share the role of protagonists. This script is the third in a trilogy about them which began with *Sarah's Play* and which includes *The Gadget*. The long and close relationship of Rex Deverell with Ken Kramer and The Globe Theatre of Regina has led to a confident style in these participation plays for elementary school children. In each of the three, Ivan creates a machine which runs amok in some manner. Audience participation is connected to the machine and the author takes advantage of this direct involvement to unleash some of his own and society's ambivalent feelings about contemporary technology as an instant answer to age-old quandaries. The portrait of Mazie, the bag lady, is affectionate and benign. We are all sorry to see her lose her individuality in the "habit removing machine" and happy when she returns to herself. The vagrant, Ben, in *More of a Family* is more menacing and perhaps reflects some differences between a small city in Saskatchewan and a big city in Manitoba.

Vandal has the least attractive and most disturbing heros— some would call them villains—but the author shows through his "framing scenes" the insidious and powerful forces outside the control of young people which nonetheless exert enormous pressures on their lives. There is refreshing wit and unsentimental understanding in the treatment of the four young people in *Vandal*. The lyrics of the original songs underscore the author's intentions. The concluding scenes are powerful and chilling and demand discussion and intelligent action toward changes in the circumstances which encourage vandalism. Although both the Deverell and Horrocks scripts are dealing with sickness in our society, they are stageworthy comedies—not sermons.

These eight plays present a cross section of contemporary issues and classic themes of concern to children and young people. All of the playwrights wrote the plays on the prairies and some plays specifically reflect prairie concerns and sensibilities. All authors are adept at enlisting the many resources unique to theatrical production and in so doing, they have created an impressive body of work in a relatively new genre—theatre for young audiences.

Joyce Doolittle
Calgary, Alberta, February 1984

Tikta'liktak
Brian Paisley

Murray McCune, **Tikta'liktak**, *and Robert Astle,* **Nanuk**,
in the 1982 Chinook Theatre Production.

photograph: T. Hallas

Tikta'liktak was first performed by Chinook Touring Theatre, Edmonton, Alberta as part of its fall tour 1982 (October 4 - December 3), with the following cast:

First Storyteller ———————————— Bonnie Green
Second Storyteller ———————————— Robert Astle
Tikta'liktak ———————————— Murray McCune

Directed by Brian Paisley

Set and costume design: Kathryn Michaud and Denis Vallee
Mask design: Carol Piercy
Lighting design: Derek Visser

Requests for performance rights should be addressed to:

Brian Paisley
51139 Range Road
Sherwood Park, Alberta
Canada T8B 1K5

With the warming spring, the ice that covers the sea begins melting. The currents, tides and winds shift and crack the ice, pushing it into ridges or breaking it apart, making wide channels and lakes of open water. At the floe edge where the land ice ends, visibility is obscured by rolling, dark grey clouds of steam as the warmer sea meets the cold air. This was a time of special danger for the hunter, when he might be crushed, or left stranded on a floe that had floated away, with no means of returning to the land . . .

Heather Smith Siska
People of the Ice

Three Inuit stranded on an ice floe off Baffin Island were rescued Saturday when skies cleared long enough for searchers to find them.

The two men and a nine-year-old boy were "safe and well" Saturday night aboard the Coast Guard icebreaker *Pierre Radisson* after the week-long ordeal, said Capt. Ron Bayer of the search and rescue co-ordination centre at Halifax, N. S.

"They were all right," said Sgt. Bob Dube, also of the rescue centre. "They shot a seal Friday so they had food."

News Item, August, 1982
Edmonton Journal

Heaven is a place where caribou graze in great herds, and they are easy to hunt . . .

In Hell people are always hungry, for their only food is butterflies.

. . . an Inuit hunter
Seasons of the Eskimo

Darkness.

A dome of white. Under the dome and in front of it a white snowscape with contours, crevices and chunks of ice.

A faint flickering from several stone lamps provides a small, warm circle of light.

Very quietly, the audience is led in by the two storytellers and seated around the snowscape in front of the dome.

When all the audience has been seated the two storytellers take each of the stone lamps and give them to a member of the audience to hold.

Story 1/Story 2: Please, take this stone lamp, this krudlik, and hold it like this. Good. Hold it carefully, don't spill the oil inside. And turn the flame toward us, this way . . . so that its light will fill our igloo. Good . . .

As the lamps are distributed the light spreads, so that the snowscape and dome glow warmly in the darkness.

When all the lamps have been handed out the two storytellers take up their drums and begin a slow beat.

The drumming grows more intense, reaches a crescendo. Silence. One drummer starts again, the other takes up the butterfly.

Story 1:
Tikta'liktak
Ayii, yaii
Ayii, yaii
Tikta'liktak

Story 2: Butterfly

Story 1: Tikta'liktak

Story 2: Butterfly

Story 1:
Tikta'liktak
Ayii, yaii
Ayii, yaii
Tikta'liktak

The butterfly flutters above the drummer.

Story 1: Tikta'liktak—the Arctic butterfly . . . And the name of a young hunter who lived with his family on the barren shores of the Arctic sea. In summer and early fall Tikta'liktak's people would hunt the swift caribou—tuktuk—with bow and arrow, taking from the carcass meat for food, bones for carving, sinews for weapons and tools, fur for warm parkas . . . No part of the animal was thrown away, the dogs finished the remains . . . Tuktuk's spirit filled the long, cold nights of winter. And Tikta'liktak's people hunted other animals as well—fox, fish, geese, seabirds, even the mighty whale. And, most important, natcherk—the seal. In the dark days when the sun does not appear, natcherk gives blubber for food and oil to light the lamps and melt the snow to water . . .

The butterfly disappears. Storyteller 1 beats the drum.

Ayii, ayii, ayii
Darkness fills my house
The caribou have fled
Fish and seal hide from me
Beneath the frozen water
My stomach shrinks
My plate is empty
Ayii, ayii, ayii

Story 2: At the end of this long winter, Tikta'liktak's people faced starvation. Last summer the caribou did not come in great numbers . . . Food became scarce, the Inuit lived on lemmings and fish and birds, but little could be stored. And now the spring would not come, the bitter winds still howled, the birds and the fish and the seals could not be found. Huge masses of ice smashed and cracked along the shore of the sea. Fog covered the land . . . It was a time of famine.

Story 1: But Tikta'liktak was young and eager, and his father was teaching him to be a clever hunter. In their igloo Tikta'liktak watched his family grow sore from hunger . . . so he made up his mind to help them. With his harpoon and his bow and arrow he set out into the pale, white wilderness . . .

The butterfly reappears, flutters around.

All of this happened . . . in the magic time . . . taitsumani . . .

Story 2: Long, long ago . . .

Story 1: Taitsumani . . .

Story 2: Long, long ago . . .

The butterfly vanishes behind a mound of snow.

The lights change, losing their warmth.

Tikta'liktak appears from behind the mound, climbing, looking around as he struggles onto the snowscape. He wears parka, boots, mitts and snow goggles—he carries a bow and arrow slung over his shoulder and a harpoon in his hands.

Tikta'liktak stands, then for a few moments he gazes back the way he has come. He raises the harpoon in salute, then turns and looks across the snowscape. He peers at the sky, then at the land. He begins to move, cautiously, feeling ahead with his harpoon, picking his way across the dangerous ice.

The drumbeats warn of thin, treacherous patches. Tikta'liktak moves slowly, sometimes smiling when he avoids a break or reaches a secure place.

Then he sees something in the snow. He moves toward it quickly, watching all directions. He kneels to examine the snow, his hand tracing a paw mark. His body tenses, his grasp tightens on the harpoon as he looks back along the trail, then ahead, the way he was going.

Tik: Nanuk.

Story 1: Nanuk.

Story 2: The great white bear.

Tikta'liktak begins to move again, even more cautiously now, always watching.

The great white bear was hungry too. Like Tikta'liktak, he searched for new hunting grounds.

Story 1: But nanuk does not move cautiously over the ice. He hunts wherever he wants to hunt—and if the ice cracks under his great weight and his huge, rolling body plunges into the freezing water his white, thick fur protects him as he claws his way back onto the snow . . .

Tik: Nanuk . . .

Story 1: Nanuk . . .

Story 2: The great white bear.

Story 1: Nanuk is hungry too.

The drums reach an ice-cracking crescendo as Tikta'liktak runs and stumbles across the snowscape. He stops, breathing heavily, weary, exhausted.

The lights change, become more pale, orange and threatening. Tikta'liktak watches the sky.

Tik: Dogs of the sun. Ayii, a storm is coming. *He shields his eyes from the light. Ayii, nangim, my people suffer.*
He buries his head. One of the drums beats ominously.
Then, behind Tikta'liktak, a distant flock of seabirds appears, half hidden in the gloom.
The drumming stops. Tikta'liktak pulls himself up and, as he does so, he sees the flock of birds. Excited now, he moves into a better position, planning his hunt, paying little attention to the cracking of the ice.
He reaches a good spot. Keeping his eyes on the seabirds he lays aside his harpoon and takes up his bow and arrows. Hastily, he fires—the drum snapping arrow after arrow—as the flock of seabirds swoops and dives.
The last arrow flies. The seabirds swoop down and disappear. Tikta'liktak leaps up, grinning broadly.
Tik: Oh,. ayii, ayii, yaii, yaii . . . Tikta'liktak is a lucky hunter.
He gathers his harpoon and pack and sets off briskly across the snowscape. The drum sound of ice cracking follows him but he is oblivious to the danger. He moves out of sight.
Story 2: Tikta'liktak's aim was true. He had killed many birds. He hurried to pick them up before they could drift away and be lost in the fog. He piled the soft, feathered birds, still warm, on the snow and searched for his last arrow . . .
Story 1: Then he saw it . . . far out on the edge of the ice . . .
Tikta'liktak reappears at the edge of the snowscape. He peers across and sees the last arrow. He makes his way across the ice.
The light wavers. The drums beat slowly, occasionally cracking loudly as Tikta'liktak makes his way toward the arrow.
He finds it—but no bird. He holds it up, grinning.
Tik: *With a chuckle.* Ah, suviitor . . . Tikta'liktak is not always so lucky.
The drums crack. The light wavers wildly. Tikta'liktak staggers about as the ice shakes beneath him. Desperately, he tries to go back the way he came, but the ice continues to crack and quake.
Finally, Tikta'liktak reaches the edge where he last appeared and he is about to go, when a last great quake throws him to the ground.
The drums stop. The light settles pale, blue, cold.
Slowly, Tikta'liktak gets to his feet. He recovers his bow, arrows

and harpoon then rushes to the edge of the snowscape. He stares out into the darkness, one direction, then another.

Tik: Akrale! The ice is broken!

He rushes across to the other side of the snowscape, slipping and falling as he goes. Again he looks out into the darkness.

The ice is broken! Ayii, ayii, ayii . . . I can't get back.

He goes to another spot on the edge, peers out, tests the water with his harpoon, staggers backward.

The sea will swallow me.

He hunches up on the ice, rocking on his heels.

Ayii, ayii, ayii . . . the sea will swallow me.

The lights grow dimmer, colder. Tikta'liktak continues to rock and shiver.

Story 1: As night pressed in on Tikta'liktak's tiny frozen island the Arctic wind rose and grew even colder . . .

Tikta'liktak stirs. He takes off his snow goggles and begins to search for some shelter. He takes out his knife and cuts and digs out some chunks of ice, leaning them together like a small tent. Then he crawls inside, huddling tight.

Tik: I must not sleep. I will not sleep.

Story 2: Sleep.

Story 1: Sleep.

The drums sound . . . slow, cracking.

Tik: I will not sleep. Ayii, yaii . . . I must not sleep.

Story 2: Sleep . . .

Story 1: Sleep . . . And freeze.

Tik: Ayii, ayii, ayii.

Story 1/Story 2: Sleep . . . Freeze . . . Wait for the ice island to crack and burst and break apart and drop Tikta'liktak into the black, freezing sea.

Tik: Ayii, yaii . . . No sleep. No sleep.

The storytellers circle Tikta'liktak's shelter, beating their drums in a rising monotonous rhythm. As the drums grow stronger, Tikta'liktak struggles to stay awake.

No sleep. No sleep, No sleep.

The drums fade as the light changes to cold, white day. Tikta'liktak struggles out of his shelter, puts on his goggles and moves to the edge of the ice. Once again he searches the darkness.

At the other side of the snowscape the seal appears. The seal moves about on the edge of the snowscape and does not notice the man opposite.

Tikta'liktak hears something, turns and sees the seal.

Tik: Ah . . . natcherk.

Quietly but quickly Tikta'liktak picks up his harpoon. He moves around the ice, keeping low—but his moves are clumsy, without patience or control. As he starts to raise his harpoon the seal turns and sees him and slips back into the sea.

Tik: Ah—natcherk . . . Come back.

He scrambles to the edge, cuts a chunk of ice and begins to scratch, imitating the sound of the seal on the ice.

Kilee . . . kilee . . . kilee . . . Come back, natcherk, come back to me . . . Kilee . . . kilee . . . kilee . . .

Tikta'liktak continues to chant.

Story 2: For most of the day Tikta'liktak remained at the edge of his ice island, trying to tempt the seal to return . . .

Tik: Kilee . . . kilee . . . kilee . . .

Story 2: He makes the sound of a seal's claws opening a breathing hole in the ice . . . if natcherk is curious, he may come back . . .

Tik: Come back . . kilee . . . kilee . . .

The raven appears, swoops at something on the ice, finds nothing, cries in annoyance.

Tikta'liktak

Tikta'liktak spins around and, seeing the raven, he scrambles after it.

Tik: Tulawak!

The bird screams and avoids him. Then it swoops out of sight. Too late, Tikta'liktak has got his bow and arrow, but the raven is not to be seen. He looks around in frustration.

Story 2: Sometimes being a good bowman is not enough. To succeed in the hunt a man must also become wise. That way the animals will give themselves to him.

Tikta'liktak has returned to his shelter. He gathers the ice chunks and begins to cover himself with ice and snow. He is almost lost from view, but then his hand appears. He places one of his mitts on the mound above him and then his hand disappears again.

Tik: *Quietly, from inside the mound.* Kilee . . . kilee . . .

The drum sounds briskly. The raven returns. Tikta'liktak falls silent.

The raven swoops about, croaking noisily. It lands once, searches the ice and finding nothing resumes its flight. Then it sees the mitt and swings over the mound. Back and forth it flies, curious, unsure. Then it sweeps down and attacks, croaking in triumph. Tikta'liktak's hand shoots up from the snow mound and he grabs the raven. The bird's croaks turn to screams as it fights to get away. The drum pounds loudly as Tikta'liktak pulls the raven down into the mound. The bird's cries cease. Silence. Tikta'liktak remains hidden from view.

Story 1: But the raven is a thin bird, a scavenger . . . and its poor flesh will not satisfy Tikta'liktak's gnawing hunger.

Tikta'liktak crawls out of his hiding place, in pain, holding his stomach.

Tik: Kadjgum!

Story 2: Hunger.

Tik: Kadjgum!

Story 2: Hunger.

Story 1: For days Tikta'liktak drifted without food or water. Often huge ice floes churned past his tiny island—some crashed against his floe . . .

The drums crack. Tikta'liktak staggers and falls. He looks up, worn and beaten.

Sometimes he could even see the mainland . . . so near, yet, without a boat, so far . . .

Tik: Eelunga. Eelunga.

Story 2: Tikta'liktak called to his family . . .

Tik: Eelunga . . .

Story 2: Many times he dreamed of his home, his family, his friends . . . but though he called to them hour after hour his only answer was the lonely moan of the wind.

Story 1: Tikta'liktak began to think that he might die.

Tik: This island is my grave. *He curls up.* Ayii, ayii, ayii . . . This island is my grave.

Tikta'liktak gets up, stumbles toward the edge of the ice. He looks out, sees something.

Tik: *Pointing.* Taikka! Look! Over there! Walrus! Fat walrus!

Kilee . . . kilee! Ah . . . the wind carries them away. Ayii, ayii, ayii . . . I shall never leave this place. I shall never leave this place.

He staggers back toward the centre of the snowscape. He looks around wildly, then begins to gather his weapons and pack. Then he cuts and gathers chunks of ice and begins to arrange them in the shape of a coffin.

Tik: *Mumbling, almost determined.* This island is my grave. My grave. My grave.

The coffin is complete. Now he arranges his tools and weapons neatly beside it.

Someday they will find me. Someday they will know. Nangim . . . my suffering . . .

He lies down in the "grave". The two storytellers begin a steady, somber beat on their drums.

The light slowly changes to night. Only the slow beat of one drum can now be heard . . . there is almost silence.

Tikta'liktak snores loudly. He shivers and pushes at the ice on top of him.

Tik: Ayii, yaii . . . I am cold!

He sits up, looks about.

I don't want to die. I do not want to join my ancestors.

He pulls at his hair.

I will not die. I will not die. I will not die.

He blows his hands, pulls and counts his fingers.

Atausik . . . mukko . . . pingasut . . . sitamut . . . tidlimut .·. . Ayii, ayii, ayii . . . I will not die.

He struggles out of the "grave", puts on his mitts, takes up his harpoon.

Fat walrus! Nanuk! Natcherk!! Kilee! Kilee! Kilee!

A single drum beats. On the other side of the snowscape—the seal reappears. Tikta'liktak sees it.

Tik: *Amazed.* Natcherk. *He starts to stumble toward it, then pulls himself under control.* No. Go slow. Think like the seal. Be like the seal. He will give his spirit to you. Ukshavok . . . It should be so.

Tikta'liktak circles warily—the seal is not aware of the hunter. As he draws closer, Tikta'liktak slinks closer to the snow and begins to move like the seal.

Think like the seal. Be like the seal.

He moves his body the same way as the seal. It turns toward him. A silence. Then Tikta'liktak scratches the ice with his "flipper". The seal makes the same kind of move. Tikta'liktak does it again, slipping even closer. The seal scratches again, then turns away. Swiftly, Tikta'liktak throws the harpoon. The seal struggles, but the blade is buried deep. Tikta'liktak pulls the harpoon line taut and holds on as the seal squirms.

Tik: Aklikat! My harpoon! Hold tight! His spirit will soon leave him!

The seal dies. Tikta'liktak pulls it in.

Ayii, ayii, ayii
Spirit of the sea
You bring me joy
Aja-ja-japape
Hu-hue! Glorious
Spirit of the sea
You bring me joy
Ayii, ayii, ayii

The drum stops. Tikta'liktak pulls the seal carcass over to his shelter. He rebuilds his ice tent and crawls inside, half-hidden from view.

Story 1: The seal brought new life to Tikta'liktak. The meat was his food—he ate and slept and ate again. His strength came back. He found a stone and carved out a lamp. He filled it with the seal's oil and started it burning by whirling an arrow into shavings from a piece of driftwood. Now he had light, and heat, as well as food.

The light is brighter now, warmer.

Story 1: The spring sun began to shine more brightly, and Tikta'liktak remembered once more that he was young.

Tikta'liktak emerges from the shelter. He looks stronger now, more confident.

Story 1: At night the sky was filled with stars . . .

The lights change, flashing with green and yellow.

And the northern lights danced and kicked like spirits at play . . .

Tikta'liktak raises his arms to the lights.

Tik: Tunrat! Spirits! Ayii, yaii . . . My suffering has ended. I tremble with joy. Atun! Atun! My song is magic. I have found a way to go home!

The lights change to white, harsh day. Tikta'liktak returns to his shelter and brings out a bag made from the seal skin.

Story 1: Tikta'liktak had built a float from the seal's skin. He had turned the skin inside out, blown it up into a bag of air and plugged it with a piece of driftwood. He planned to set out across the sea and let the tide carry him back to land . . .

The drum beats ominously.

But the smell of the dead seal had already drifted far across the ice . . . *Tikta'liktak is busy at his pack. On the other side of the snowscape, the polar bear appears, pulling himself up onto the ice floe. Tikta'liktak has not heard him. The bear moves up behind him and, at the last second, Tikta'liktak senses the beast and flings himself sideways. As he falls he grabs the harpoon, then he scrambles away. The bear sniffs and prods the sealskin pack as Tikta'liktak watches from a distance.*

The polar bear pushes the pack away when he finds there is nothing to eat. He turns toward Tikta'liktak. He watches him.

Tik: Nanuk.

The bear growls as if in reply, low and menacing. Tikta'liktak checks his harpoon, but it is a small weapon. The bear growls again, preparing to attack.

Tik: Think like the bear. Be like the bear.

Tikta'liktak moves slowly away, until he finds a suitable crevice in the ice. Then he wedges the harpoon in, its blade pointing out and up, toward the bear.

The bear circles. Then with a roar it charges. Tikta'liktak holds his position until the last possible moment and the bear reaches out for him. Tikta'liktak falls away and the bear plunges on to the harpoon.

But the bear is not dead. It stumbles to regain its balance, but the harpoon is buried deep. It turns again toward Tikta'liktak.

Tik: Aklikat! My harpoon! Stick deep! His spirit will rush out!

The bear makes one final heave toward him, but the effort is its last. With a coughing sigh, the polar bear dies.

Tikta'liktak staggers forward and grabs his knife. Exhausted, he kneels beside the dead bear.

Tik: Nanuk.

He plunges the knife in, cuts. Then he lies beside the carcass. The lights darken.

Story 2: From the great white bear Tikta'liktak had more meat— meat for his journey home. And from the bear's warm, white fur,

Tikta'liktak made himself a warm, soft blanket to sleep away his last nights on the ice . . .

The light changes to a pale, cold dawn. Tikta'liktak rises, drags the bear carcass away and buries it in the snow. He carries a new paddle back to his harpoon and sealskin pack.

Story 1: And from the shoulder blade bone of nanuk, Tikta'liktak fashioned a strong paddle.

He lashes the paddle to the end of his harpoon.

Tikta'liktak picks up his pack and his harpoon and his paddle and moves toward the far side of the snowscape. The drums start as he disappears from view.

Story 1:
Ayii, ayii, ayii
There is fear
In facing death
Alone
On an island of ice
I am free
Ayii, ayii, ayii

The lights change—the snowscape is bathed in blue light. A cold sea.

There is joy
In going home
Alive
Carried by wind and tide
I am free
Ayii, ayii, ayii

Tikta'liktak pushes himself into view. He clings to the pack and propels himself forward with the harpoon/paddle. He looks ahead.

Tik: *Pointing.* Nuna! Nuna! Land!

The drum sounds with a different beat—a dull thudding sound.

With a great, grunting roar the walrus raises its head in the water.

Tik: Akrale! Walrus! Fat bull walrus!

Frantically, Tikta'liktak paddles away. But his progress is slow. The walrus dips and rises with the tide, drawing closer.

Tik: Walrus! Blind bull walrus! I am not one of you! I am not after your herd! I am a man! I am inuk . . . a man!

With a great roar the walrus rises again. Very close to Tikta'liktak this time. Tikta'liktak raises his harpoon, but then sees the paddle is lashed to the end.

Tik: Ah . . . I cannot fight!

Then, from behind him, comes another great bellowing sound, and another, younger bull walrus appears.

The old bull brushes past Tikta'liktak, knocking him aside as the younger bull closes in.

Tikta'liktak scrambles away as the two bulls lock tusks and begin a fight to the death. As they fight, they move toward the back of the snowscape. At last, with great howling roars, they disappear beneath the waters.

Tikta'liktak has managed to make his way to the edge of the seascape. Suddenly, he stands, wavering.

Tik: Nuname! Nuname! I am on land!

He spins and collapses back onto the snow. The lights change abruptly back to the warm glow of a spring day.

The two storytellers move forward as Tikta'liktak squirms on the ground.

Story 1: Like a beached fish, Tikta'liktak felt the solid rock beneath him. He slept all of one day, ate some of his food, drank some fresh water from a nearby stream, slept another day.

Story 2: And as he slept he dreamt of his home and his family and he was filled with gratitude that the spirits who watch over the land and the sea and the sky had allowed him to make his dangerous journey.

Tikta'liktak stirs, pulls himself up to a sitting position. He gazes toward the edge of the snowscape and begins to smile.

Story 1: Tikta'liktak felt the soft tundra, watched the sun bright in the sky, saw small flowers bursting into bloom and . . .

Tik: *Pointing, rising.* Tuktuk!

Story 2: Caribou.

Tik: Tuktuk! *He scrambles to his feet.* Tuktuk!

Story 2: The caribou had returned to the land of the Inuit.

Tikta'liktak spins, grins, sits and rocks merrily.

Tik:
Ayii, yaii
I am filled with joy
I live
I live

And a great light
Fills the world
Ayii, yaii
Ayii, yaii

The drum patters. Above and behind Tikta'liktak, the butterfly appears. It flutters about, near him. He looks up and sees it.

Tik: Ah . . . Tikta'liktak.

The butterfly moves toward the far back. Tikta'liktak gathers his gear and follows it.

Lead me home, tikta'liktak . . .

Story 1: And the butterfly guided Tikta'liktak back to his own valley, back to his family who had almost given him up for dead . . .

Tikta'liktak has followed the butterfly to the edge of the back. It disappears and he clambers up on to a small rise. He looks off and waves his harpoon.

Tik: Eelunga! *He is seen.* Eelunga!! I have returned!

He scrambles down behind the rise and vanishes from sight.

The drums beat together.

Story 2: So Tikta'liktak was reunited with his family, and his mother and his father wept with happiness that their son had returned safely. His sisters made him a soft bed of caribou skins and he slept, peacefully, at last, in his own igloo.

Story 1: But often, late at night, he dreamt of his other icy island home and the crack of the floes and the roll of the sea still rocked his body. The island had become part of his soul and the mist and the tide and the wind haunted his mind like a ghost . . .

The drums rise to a crescendo . . .

A silence . . .

The lights fade, leaving only the lamps to flicker in the darkness.

■

Cornelius Dragon
Jan Truss

Cornelius Dragon was the result of conversations between Jan Truss and Gerry Thurston, Director of Caravan Theatre Calgary (1974-1977). Although the script still awaits its first full production, a workshop of the script occurred as part of the coursework in Theatre for Young Audiences taught by Joyce Doolittle at the University of Calgary in 1983.

Characters
Cornelius Dragon—a teenage boy
Three children—one with LOVE printed large on her T-shirt
Father
Mother
Kathy—a teenage girl
Woman 1
Woman 2
Cowboy
Voice 1
Voice 2
Voice 3
Circus Girl—dancer, bareback rider
Circus Bill—ringmaster
Person—a teenage girl

The settings—home, school, town, country, and circus—are created by property and costume changes.

Requests for performance rights should be addressed to:

Jan Truss
Box 8
Water Valley, Alberta
Canada   T0M 2E0

Cornelius Dragon stands looking out of window as audience settles. He is relaxed and hatless. The other three actors seated at side. Red hunting cap on a nail in window frame.

Choosing moment to begin, Cornelius touches wind chime—the first sound. Pause. Cornelius assumes his character. Touches wind chime more firmly. As sound settles he turns to speak to audience. A nonchalant, easy stance.

Cornelius: Hi. I'm Cornelius Dragon. Crazy name, eh? Could have been worse though. When we first moved to Canada—I was just a little guy then—we were called Dragonoffskiwitch. How does that grab you? Can you imagine—Cornelius Dragonoffskiwitch!

Thank goodness my father officially got the name changed. Not much better for a kid though. Dragon. Wow, I'm telling you—the things parents do to little kids. My full name—even after the change—Cornelius Horatio Dragon.

Then they dressed me up in those short little pants—leather, you know—real short. With embroidered suspenders. Embroidered with flowers. Pink. Red. Pale blue. Purple. On those fancy suspenders—flowers—

My father, poor old guy, he'd been a tailor back where they came from. Who needed a tailor here? Everybody wore blue jeans. So my father, well, he got to be the school janitor—see. Pushing a broom.

Cornelius showing discomfiture. He picks up broom and begins sweeping. He puts on the red hunting cap and pulls it forward on his forehead.

Pushing a broom—pushing a broom. And I used to help him.

Cornelius laughs nervously. Loses manliness. Becomes a boy.

Scary at night in the empty school when I was left there by myself. Swishing noises down the long corridors. Pipes gurgled like monsters. A mouse ran. Something touched the window.

Cornelius laughs, remembering.

I was just little—then.

In the pause before 'I was just little,' Love, Boy and Skirt take a child's hat each from the hat tree and become little kids. Love creeps around stage pointing and mocking. Love, Boy and Skirt move around Cornelius, taunting, chanting.

Love: Corny, corny, Cornelius.

Boy: Yah, yah, shorty pants, shorty pants.

Love: Pretty, pretty flowers.

Skirt: Janitor boy, dirty, dirty.

Love, Boy, Skirt dance around him holding their noses.

Chorus: Stinky, stinky, Janitor boy. Stinky—pooh.

Love: He washes the toilets.

Chorus: Pooh.

Love, Boy, Skirt, running farther away and pointing, screaming with laughter. Cornelius hunches over his broom, sweeping.

Love: Oh, oh, does his mummy put pretty flowers on his panties then.

Chorus: Pretty sissy, pretty sissy.

Love: His mother don't speaky the language.

Boy: His momma crazy, crazy.

Chorus: Crazy momma, big crazy momma.

Skirt: She don't speaky the language proper.

Skirt affects a strong accent. Speaks like a mother calling her child down the block with mocking accent.

Cornelius. Cornelius   Horatio   Dragon.

Love, Boy, Skirt, pointing and screaming with laughter.

Chorus: Cornelius - Dragon - Dragon - Dragon -

Boy: Look at the scared dragon.

Chorus: Scared, scaredy pants, shorty pants, pooh dragon pooh pooh pooh.

Love, Boy, Skirt, hold noses, point, taunting. Cornelius can take no more. His anger bursts. He rushes at his taunters violently with the broom. They scatter, ducking, holding their noses, pointing.

Boy: He cleans toilets.

Chorus: Pooh.

Love: Stinky dragon.

Chorus: Pooh . . . pooh . . . pooh.

Cornelius swings broom around as though he will cut off their legs. They have to jump over it. He is very fast and they have to jump several times before they get away. When they do get away he stands on guard with his broom threatening them, growling.

Cornelius: Aaaah   Aaaah   Come on, fight, I dare you!   aaah
aaah—

Love, Boy, Skirt try to back off without losing face, point and grimace but back off, until they have their arms round each other, whispering, giggling, fade back onto their chairs to become the waiting actors. Cornelius gets control of himself, calms down. The actors take off their kid's hats.

Cornelius leans on broom as though about to speak. Pushes hat up on forehead. Pushes broom to window, pauses sadly. Runs fingers contemplatively across wind chime. Sweet sound. Sanity. Pauses. Turns to speak to audience.

Cornelius: Who'd ever want to be a kid? A funny little kid, at that. Wonder if it's hard for all kids. Sure was for me. Cornelius Horatio Dragon. Short pants. Flowers. Pushing a broom. Poor crazy parents. They didn't know. Parents. My parents—

Cornelius shakes head sadly. Leans on broom. Watches Boy and Skirt hang up their kid's hats and take on role of Mother and Father.

Skirt ties a black scarf tightly round her head and picks a black shawl from the clothes tree. She winds herself in shawl. Boy, simultaneously, takes a plaid janitor's cap, pulls it firmly on, takes an old-fashioned jacket from the clothes tree and wears it. As they change clothes they age visibly, slowly, becoming pathetic, but proud. Mother and Father pick up a chair each and set them together centrally.

As they sit down, Cornelius leaves broom, walks out to other side of window, a boy looking in to his home, watching. Mother knits, Father and Mother glance at each other with irritation. Then look away. They embody discomfort, misery. Father bursts out irritably—with some accent.

Father: Woman—you should get out more. Dress like the other women. Talk to people so you learn to speak the language.

Mother: You at me am speak like this. You dare—so speak at me, your wife. No—uttermutter garishachnach—

Mother finishes in a burst of gibberish. Father covers ears.

Father: Woman, Woman, please, please speak in English. This is Canada. I am ashamed that you do not learn the language. You make us all look foolish. You do not try. I am ashamed. Everybody, everybody laugh at us because of you. I am shamed.

Mother: Bah. Me shame also . . . also. I not sweeping man wed. Jan - Jan-i-tor no person is. I not jan-i-tor wed. Before proud I was

. . . proud woman . . . aaah. Proud I was my head to lift in blessed cathedral. Proud aaah, with strong stone house . . . safe . . . strong. High rooms and springtime . . . cherry trees. Now . . . aach . . . wooden shack and snow . . . always snow. All winter here . . . always winter. I was proud woman . . . proud—

Father: Oh . . . I know, you think I do not know? But, my dear, you will be proud again. It takes time to make a new life.

Mother: Proud. I learn word PROUD. Baah. Also my son janitor - sweeper boy you would make. I hate. I weep. Baaaah.

Father: We have to eat. Any work is better than no work. Who needs the fine suit, the fancy shirt here? These hands must work, for you—for my son—for the future— No work is degrading. Only the way you do it. I am a good janitor. Cornelius he does a good job too.

Mother: My son . . . my son, janitor.

Father: He will not always be a janitor. He is clever. He will go to university . . . I will work hard for him.

Mother: Yes. Yes. My Cornelius clever, clever boy. He will make well. Oh, my dear, what to us happen is. New country we say so good would be.

Father: It's not so bad. Enough to eat. No police, no soldiers at the door. We speak our minds—almost. For Cornelius this will be the land of opportunity.

Mother: Yes, yes, I hope . . . I pray.

Cornelius leaves the outside window. Mother and Father sway in reconciliation. Cornelius approaches them with a yellow report card in one hand and a yellow flower in the other.

Cornelius: Momma.

Cornelius gives Mother the flower. He gives Father the report card.

Cornelius: Poppa.

Mother: Cornelius, my Cornelius, you should not the first flower of springtime pluck. Report card you bring. It good, yes? No?

Cornelius: Not bad, Momma.

Father: Not bad.

Mother: Not bad you say. Not bad is not good. Not good—

Mother hysterically snatches the report. Father tries to protest.

Father: Now, my dear.

Mother: H in mathematics. Excellent. That is good . . . Yes? H in science. Excellent student. That is good . . . No? What is this? This?

What is this? C in guidance and family living. Who gets C in this? Who? Who? Who? Only C. We do not raise you right, yes? No?

Father: Come, come, what is this guidance? This family living? Does it go to university? No. No it does not. So, who cares?

Mother: My son. One C is bad. I shame. And what is this? A, A only in English. Only A. English important is for university. Why you not make H? You no good. Lazy, Not work. I shame—

Cornelius: Oh, Momma. A is not bad.

Mother: Cornelius, not bad you say. I tell you not bad is not good. I shame.

Cornelius: I did my best. Momma I tell you I did my best. How loud must I shout to make you believe. I did my best.

Mother: Baaaah. Call this best. You should shamed be. Your father and me we work, work, work, work for you, for university. Lazy you. Disgrace. You disgrace. A. Only A in most important English language. Larry Thomas he work. Larry Thomas he get H in English I know . . . Larry Thomas work . . . work.

Cornelius: Oh yeah. Larry Thomas' mother speaks English—real good.

Father: How dare you shout at your mother like this. You like it when I shout at you?

Cornelius: She has no right to shout these things at me. I do my best, don't I?

Father: Don't you shout at me. You could work harder. I know you spend too much time daydreaming in the fields. Too much time chasing girls.

Cornelius: Too much time doing your rotten janitor work.

Father: You dare say that to me. You . . . You . . .

Father slaps Cornelius across the face. Cornelius clenches his fists, impotently raging.

Mother and Father remove their chairs, slowly remove the parent clothes, hang them up. Mother has dropped the yellow flower on the floor.

Cornelius strides to the wind chimes, jangles them, crash, crash, crash. His rage subsides. He picks up the flower. Touches its petals. Smells it. Shrugs.

Cornelius: The first flower of springtime. Do not pick. Too much time in the fields. Where else is there for me to go for me to be alone. Too much time chasing girls. That IS a laugh.

Cornelius removes cap. Hangs it back on its nail. Touches wind chimes gently.

Too much time chasing girls. My parents didn't know much, did they? Oh no—

Cornelius takes party hat from clothes tree, hat with Love Me Quick *printed on it. From under the hat a balloon rises with a smiling face, tied to clothes tree. Cornelius wears party hat.*

There was this dance, see. A carnival dance with funny hats. Everybody dressed nice.

Cornelius watches while the others pick hats from the clothes tree. Each party hat releases balloons that rise on strings above the tree. The two girls take long skirts—these too release tethered balloons.

The three actors assume the characters of nubile teenagers dancing, snapping their fingers to make a strong beat. They dance, separate and jazzy, filling the stage. Cornelius confides in audience.

I'd put this stuff on my face to hide my spots. Washed my hair. Got a new shirt. My dad let me buy a shirt. I was glad. The shirts my dad made were always different. I hated them—because they were different.

Cornelius pulls at his collar, remembering.

Didn't like to tell my dad about his shirts. Anyhow, I'd got a new shirt like everybody else's. Deodorant. Aftershave, everything—the lot. Tonight I was going to ask Kathy to dance.

Dancers arrange themselves in group distant from Cornelius, an integrated group, laughing, happy.

A phantom crowd consisting of masks and diaphanous, flowing stuff attached to poles is brought on stage to enlarge the group. Dancers assume the characters of Kathy, Larry and Skirt. Larry and Kathy are at front of group. A pole of crowd is put into Skirt's hand. She sways with it behind Larry and Kathy. A stage hand holds other poles to make a swaying, diaphanous crowd.

Cornelius: I could see her across there in the crowd with her hair all shiny. And a new dress that was soft so you couldn't help looking right at her figure, you know. Wow, she was pretty, laughing, happy, talking to everybody. Tonight—I was going to ask her. Tonight—I had to do it. I'd promised myself. There was no backing down.

I looked at her talking to Larry Thomas. Waving her hands as she talked. Larry Thomas who got H's in everything. Did everything. Did everybody—he said.

Anyhow, I was going to ask her.

I started to walk across the auditorium floor. It seemed like everybody was on the other side. And everybody was watching me. What if I fell over on the slippery stuff they put on the floor?

As Cornelius talks he clowns his feelings.

Is my fly undone? Does the stuff on my spots show? Are my pants too tight? Nicked in someplace? Or not tight enough? Baggy? Bet I've gone all red. Crazy hat. Should I take it off. No. Everybody else's wearing crazy hats. Pretend you don't care—so what! Everybody's laughing. Feels like they're all laughing at me. Staring at me. Except Kathy. She's pretending she hasn't seen me coming. But I can't stop now. Touch her to make her look. Gee— she smells nice. Everything goes quiet. Everybody's listening. "Kathy. Kathy, wantodance?" My voice like a shout in silence. Everybody hears. I have to say it again. "Kathy, wantodance?"

She stops what she's saying to Larry Thomas. She gives me one sick look and she steps back.

Kathy: You've got to be kidding,

Cornelius: She says.

Kathy/Cornelius: You've got to be kidding,

Cornelius: She says. And Larry Thomas laughs. And she laughs. And everybody bursts out laughing.

Everybody laughs. Music swells thick with laughter. Cornelius tries to laugh. Tries to join the dancers as everybody moves spiritedly, with the phantom dancers gyrating madly. To the heavy beat of the music the dancers chant in a scene of madness.

Everybody: You've got to be kidding. You've got to be kidding.

Repeat and repeat to build to a climax.

Cornelius tries to get out from among the dancers, but always they contain him. He becomes a strange phantom dancer caught in madness. Eventually Cornelius gives up trying to escape and stands defeated with his hands over his face. The dance subsides. The dancers kiss and give the poles to stagehands.

Cornelius remains with hands over face. The dancers remove party clothes and hang them up, leaving balloons flying, all the while snapping their fingers in a slow rhythm. Working in a macabre dance round the tragic figure of Cornelius, they put on Mother and Father clothes and the child's hat. The phantom dancer poles are handed back to the dancers and a new dance with new words develops, dance like a bad dream. The dancers chant.

Child: Corny, corny Cornelius.

Father: Work, work, work, work Cornelius, work, work, work.

Mother: Not bad is not good. Not bad is not good.

Child: Washes the toilets, flush, flush, pooh.

Father: Push the broom, push the broom.

Child: Shorty pants.

Mother: Larry Thomas.

Father: Work.

Everybody: Larry Thomas. Haich. Haich. Haich. Kathy. Dance. Dance. Dance. You got to be kidding. You got to be kidding. Kidding, kidding, kidding.

The sound has reached frenzy. Cornelius breaks. He screams.

Cornelius: Aaaaaah.

All movement and sound freeze. Cornelius rushes at the wind chimes. Strikes them in madness. He picks up a stick with a nail in the end. Moves in fury.

Get out. Get out all of you. Get out.

Mother, Father, Child back away from him. Stagehands take the poles away. Mother, Father, Child sit. Withdrawn.

Cornelius fighting mad, flails and slashes the balloon faces, slashes each one to burst and bang. He is shouting.

I'm getting out of here. I've had enough. I'm getting out. Running away from all this shit. Leaving. Getting out. Getting out.

After the last balloon bang he hits savagely at the wind chimes and rushes out of sight.

Mechanically, expressionlessly, the three actors hang up character hats and clothes. The male goes out of sight. The two females put on busy-body-lady hats and important fur wraps. They become Woman 1 and Woman 2.

Woman 1: Well, have you heard the news, Mrs. Thomas?

Woman 2: You mean Cornelius Dragon?

Woman 1: Fancy him running away like that.

Woman 2: After how good this community's been to him.

Woman 1: Missing person he is now.

Woman 2: On the police files.

Woman 1: Wanted.

Woman 2: I should think so. Doing all that damage.

Woman 1: They say he went mad.

Woman 2: Well, you have to be sorry for his poor mother.

Woman 1: Not that I like her, you know.

Woman 2: But this is enough to kill the poor thing.

Woman 1: Yes. I guess we should send her a card.

Woman 2: Yes, take up a collection. In the drug store?

Woman 1: Yes. And buy her six roses.

Woman 2: Red or yellow do you think.

Woman 1: Oh white. Definitely white for her case.

Woman 2: Get a nice card. Get everybody to sign it.

Woman 1: Is there a card for when a kid runs away?

Woman 2: You'd think so. There's a card for everything.

Woman 1: So you say the right thing.

Woman 2: Yes. Never to offend.

Woman 1: If there isn't, should we send her a sympathy card?

Woman 2: Perhaps he isn't dead.

Woman 1: A get-well card wouldn't be right either.

Woman 2: Strange boy he was. I never did like the look of him.

Woman 1: Best wishes might be okay.

Woman 2: Along with six roses.

Woman 1: White.

Woman 2: Not that I like her, you know.

Woman 1: No, I know what you mean. She's not my type.

Woman 2: I've never liked any of the Dragon family, if I'm honest.

Woman 1: Good riddance, I'd say, if they all went back.

Woman 2: I couldn't agree more. Back where they came from—wherever that was.

Woman 1: But everybody will want to send her a card.

Woman 2: Take up a collection today.

Woman 1: Six roses.

Woman 2: White.

Woman 1: And a pretty little card from all of us.

Woman 2: Just to show how we care.

Woman 1 and Woman 2 maintaining character hang up their costumes and go out of sight.

Pause—sound of dry summer wind. Distant whinnying. Cowboy—looming larger than life, staggers under a burning sun. He carries a large, flashy saddle and saddlebags. He is a roistering, macho figure.

Cowboy: Phew. It's hot.

Cowboy walks around searching the horizon. Sets the saddle down centrally, facing front. Wipes sweat off himself, all the time scanning the landscape.

Damn horse. I'll break his back if I ever catch him. Teach the devil to get away on me. What the heck got into the creature, taking off in this God-forsaken desert of a place. Phew . . . Hills as bald as smooth as brass balls. Dry country, man, dry.

Cowboy listens to horizon. Cups his hands to his mouth and calls into distance.

Here boy. Here boy. Come up King. Come up, up, up, King.

Cowboy whinnies, the sound spreading and echoing faintly.

Kin-in-in-in-ing.

Cornelius walks into scene showing exhaustion. His shirt is open to the belly. His pants rolled up. He comes up to the Cowboy from behind as Cowboy scans the horizon. Cowboy is startled. Cornelius is dazed.

Cornelius: Hi mister.

Cowboy: Well I'll be damned. What the devil are you doing here? Seen my horse?

Cornelius: What d'ya say mister? Horse? Where? Cactus. Look out. Draws blood. Prickles claw. Tear. Blood. *Acts as though to fend off cactus and thorns. He acts out his thoughts, jumping back from the gopher, following the path of the dragonfly with his finger.* Gopher. Look out. Dragonfly, Bzzzz. Wheee. What sort of horse, mister, what sort of a horse?

Cowboy: *Bemused by the boy, yet full of his own affairs.* Black stallion, kid. Best you ever saw—or are ever likely to see. Silver mane.

Cowboy thinks he sees something on horizon. Cornelius looks to where the cowboy is looking but has to fight against buckling legs. He is struggling against collapse.

Cornelius: Whatya call him, mister?

Cowboy gets into his story, living it. Cornelius sways during the telling, struggling not to give way, but his legs give way and he ends up on his knees, looking up at Cowboy, but punctuates the

Cowboy's monologue by being distracted by a dragonfly, the path of which he traces with finger and eyes.

Cowboy: King. What's what I call him. The name I give the devil creature. King, d'you hear. KING. Real name—the name before I got him—Kingfisher. Some name eh? Some name.

Got him from a dame. Crazy dame, giving a horse a name like that. Kingfisher. Have you ever heard one better than that?

Crazy dames. All alike. This crazy dame couldn't afford to keep her fine Kingfisher. Her pasture 'd all dried up; dry, dry year.

She'd got to raise some cash to pay up the mortgage on her old man's farm or taxes or something. Jeeze, some mighty fine horseflesh they got there—I'm telling you—back there. Two days back there.

Some spread. Must 'a bin filthy rich sometime—years ago. Drought changing all that. Years o' drought. Reckon that dame was glad to sell me anything. Desperate she were. And glad, glad o' my filthy money. Yeah, glad—she had no choice—to sell this stallion to me. Took my pick, I did. Yes sir, took my pick. There they all was nibblin' and a-nuzzlin' on this 'ere cracked dry land. Picking at any slip o' leaf that showed up. Horses so sleek you wouldn't believe.

"That's the one I'll take," I says, pointing to the black stallion. The best of a fine bunch. I laughs to see the look on her face. "The one with the silver mane," I said.

She says, "Oh no," like a proper lady dame. And I heard her breath come sharp.

"Oh yeah, that's the one for me," said I again. "The one with the silver mane."

"Kingfisher," she said real soft and I nearly bust for laughing. Who in hell's name but a fool dame 'ud give a hoss a name like that?

Anyhow, "Kingfisher," she called in her lady voice, an' he came like a lamb, ate out of her hand, like, though there weren't nothing there to eat. Laugh eh?

Well, I give her most o' my winnings from the crap game night before. Most emptied my wallet for the silly bitch. Then with her own lady hands, she helped me take the saddle off my worn out bitch of a mare. Then this Kingfisher stood like a lamb while we put my saddle on him. And we headed south, Kingfisher and me.

Ornery crowbait critter, took some holdin'. But I drove him, man, I drove him. Kept him hobbled when we wasn't goin'. Festerin' piece of horseflesh broke his hobble while I was catchin' a night's sleep. Got away on me—ornery son of a dog's dinner. Kid, you didn't see him making his way north, did ya? Did ya, boy?

Cornelius: Didn't see anything mister, 'cept gophers. And dragonflies. Like divebombers. Whhheee - eoooooo. And the sun . . . Was looking for a river to cool my feet . . . or a place to eat . . . or . . . a truck for a ride. Dragonflies . . . wheeee - eoooooo. *Collapses, head to ground, arms outstretched.*

Cowboy: Hey, you okay kid? Sun getting to you, eh?

Cornelius: Put your ear to the ground. You can hear hooves. Thudding . . . thudding . . . thudding . . . thudding.

Cowboy: Honest. Is that so? *Whinnies. Pauses to listen.* Kin-in-in-g. Come up boy, come up—up—up. King— Kin-in-ing.

Cowboy takes off hat, sifts fingers on earth to find pebbles. Puts pebbles in hat. Shakes hat to make sound of oats to the distance, as he calls. King. Here King. King— Kin-in-ing.

Cornelius: *Calls from down on earth, an eerie call, long drawn out.* Kingfisher.

Sound. A distant, eerie neighing.

Did you hear that mister?

Cowboy: No kid. Hear what? I didn't hear nothing. Did you hear him? Here King. Here King boy. Kin-in-ing.

Cornelius: Kingfisher. Kingfisher.

Sound. Neighs from opposite directions one after the other.

There. There. There he is. Here he comes. Thud. Thud. Beating of my heart.

Cowboy: Where? Where? Don't see nothing. Don't hear nothing. King—Kin-in-ing. King.

Cornelius: Kingfisher—Kingfisher—

Cornelius laughs. Whinnying sounds from all directions. Cornelius' laughing plays amongst the whinnies.

Sounds like they're getting closer.

Cowboy: *Gets down with ear to ground.* Where? Where? I don't hear nothing. Here, here Boy. Here King—

Cornelius: Kingfisher.

Cornelius laughs and laughs mingle with whinnies.

Cowboy: I don't hear nothing.

Cornelius: Thud. Thud. Thud-thud-thud . . . thud . . . thud . . . thudding. Kingfisher. *Whinnies then laughs.* Closer. Closer.

Cowboy: *Ear to ground. Leg up kicking.* I don't hear nothing. Nothing.

Cornelius: You got to call a kingfisher a kingfisher. A king is not a kingfisher. A kingfisher is not a king.

Cornelius whinnies far and wide.

A Kingfisher is a bird. Fly free. Fly high. Dragonflies bombing the sun. Wheee - eoooooo. Kingfisher.

Cornelius whinnies urgently. Crawls on all fours, making like a horse, neighing and tossing his head.

Cowboy: Hey kid, you all right? Here. You'd better cover your head with my hat. The sun must of gotten to you. You shouldn't be out in the sun like this without a hat.

Cowboy puts his hat on Cornelius and as he talks gets a flask from his saddlebag. Holds Cornelius up and pours liquor into him. Cornelius coughs and struggles at first, then guzzles with abandon.

Here kid, I've got just the stuff you need. This'll cure you. This'll do you good fella. Put hair on your chest. This sorts out the men from the boys.

Cornelius: The hooves are in my ears - thud - thud - thudthudthud

Cowboy: When did you last eat boy?

Cornelius: Two . . . three days . . . dunno . . . wheee-eooooo—

Cowboy: *Takes swig from flask then passes it to Cornelius.* Say kid—you wouldn't have cash—money—the green stuff—would you?

Cornelius: *Warmed by liquor, brags.* Sure I have money. Plenty of money. What's money!

Cowboy: Sure kid, what's money? Here, drink up to good health. *Gets another flask from saddlebag.* I drink. You drink. Plenty more where that came from. Drink up kid.

Cornelius: Sure do have plenty of money. Five hundred and two dollars and twenty-seven cents. Supposed to be for going to university. Who needs it, eh? Ya - hoooo. *Full of drunken bravado, rattles loose change in a pocket, pulls out a fat wallet and waves it about.* Ya-hooo.

Cowboy: Say kid, you never did tell me your name.

Cornelius: Jim Black. That's me. Plain Jim Black.

Cowboy: Here put your hand in mine boy. Put it here. Jake Scott, your pal. Jake Scott, that's me. Your pal.

Cornelius and Cowboy shake long and sentimentally—drunkenly.

Drink on it, pal. Drop o' good stuff, eh?

Cornelius: Good stuff.

Cowboy: Damn fool broad giving a hoss a name like that. *Calls mockingly.* Kingfisher-Kingfisher-Kin-in-ing-fishshsheeer.

Cornelius: I'll drink to that—fool broad. All broads are fools.

Cowboy: They're all alike.

Cornelius: All alike.

Cowboy: Who needs 'em?

Cornelius: Yeah, yeah, who needs 'em.

Cowboy: Gimme a horse any day.

Cornelius: Yeah—yeah—gimme a horse any day—

Cowboy: Then up—up into the saddle boy. It's a man's life this.

Cornelius straddles the saddle, rocking. Cornelius and Cowboy drink again.

Cornelius: *Flourishes spurs and an imaginary whip, riding.* Ride 'em cowboy—ride 'em—Yippeeee.

Cowboy stands, legs apart, behind Cornelius, whipping and spurring, dipping from side to side, making a wild ride.

Cowboy: Yippeeee, ride man ride—

Cornelius: Ride man ride. Thud-thud-thudding in my head. Yippeee.

Cowboy: Show 'em a real man's life with a spur and a whip.

Cornelius: Yippeeee . . . yippeeee.

Cowboy: Keep moving brother.

Cornelius: Yippee . . . yippeeee. Thunder past mountains.

Cowboy: Raise us some dust.

Cowboy/Cornelius: Yippeeee.

Cornelius: *Confuses the saddle with an airplane which he revs like a motorbike, then uses like a bomber.* Brrrrrr   Brrrrrr

Cowboy: Whipping and spurring.

Cornelius: Wheee-eoooooooooou.

Cowboy: Yippeee . . . yipppeee.

Cornelius: Dragonflies bombing the sun . . . wheee - eooooou. *Falls off the saddle and rolls over, muttering.*

Kingfisher . . . Kingfisher. Wheeeee. *Out stone cold.*

Cowboy: *Slowing down, petering out.* Ride 'em cowboy . . . yippeeee.

Looks down at Cornelius, studying him. Then scans horizon for horse. No hell of a rider. Out stone cold.

Kingfisher. Fine lady's bastard. I was taken—cheated. He's got away on me. I was taken, real taken, I guess. But lady luck comes back to the gambler. Boy—you're lucky for me. Good luck, boy. See, luck ain't always a lady. No sir. Jim Black, kid, you comed along just right. You're young, kid, you won't suffer none. Your legs are strong. You got lots of tomorrows kid. A mile or so across there there's a two-bit town. You'll find it—or it'll find you.

I'll get me another horse—damn and blast Kingfisher.

Cowboy turns Cornelius over and touches the wallet protruding from his pocket. Cowboy has a second thought. He gets food and a spotted kerchief from saddlebags. Sets food out near Cornelius.

Never say I weren't a loving man. Kind—and gentle.

Won't be able to say I didn't do right by you, Jim Black. Leave him what's left of the liquor too. Good deal that. Nobody can't never say but that Jake Peters was not a fair man.

Left my wife the kids - didn't I? Left the kids a dog - didn't I? Left you a meal, kid - didn't I? *Takes wallet and looks into it.* Sorry kid, got to get me a horse - didn't I?

Hey, look at this willya. This beats all. You got to be kidding. Cornelius . . . Horatio . . . Dragon. You got to be kidding. You got to be kidding.

Come on, Cornelius Horatio Dragon, got to get going. Sorry, Jim Black. Need the hat myself, got to protect myself agin the sun—But never say I weren't a loving man.

Cowboy spreads spotted kerchief over Cornelius' head. Cowboy gathers up his things and staggers out through the audience scanning the horizon and whistling as he goes.

Cornelius remains outstretched. Actress in skirt walks on unseeing, sad, collects headscarf and shawl, transforms herself into mother. She picks up and carries a sympathy card and six white roses. Mother stands stoic and impassive while radio voices blare out the news.

Voice 1: Youth attacks service-station attendant. Gets away with more than five hundred dollars.

Voice 2: Hitch-hiker killed last night on the number five highway south. Name withheld pending identification.

Voice 3: Woman motorist attacked last night by hitch-hiker just outside Drumheller.

Voice 2: Unemployment reaches all time high.

Voice 1: Students stand little chance of finding summer jobs.

Voice 2: Hurricane causes havoc and takes lives. Many unaccounted for.

Voice 3: Flash floods sweep away highway and sections of town. Many bodies not recovered.

Voice 1: Police in B.C. report finding body of young man in the Fraser Canyon.

Voice 2: Young Canadian male held on drug charges in Mexican jail.

Mother walks away with roses and card. Head bowed.

Cornelius stirs, groans, turns on back, makes patterns across the sky with spotted kerchief.

Cornelius: Dragonflies. Blue wings flashing in the sun. I was dreaming . . . Kingfisher . . . I remember . . . Kin-in-ing Fishshsher . . . Hey Jake . . . Jake . . . where are you?

Cornelius explores his mouth. Sips from flask, not liking taste, puts flask down. Reacts to food—realizes implications of its being left. Feels for his wallet, searches ground, goes through stages of panic, horror, resignation. Now, Cornelius is a scanner of the horizon. Holds head, appeals to heaven, puts food in kerchief, starts walking, finally walking out down the aisle through audience.

Sure is a long way to nowhere—Jim Black. Walk, walk, keep walking—Jim Black.

As Cornelius leaves, the girl with Love on her chest enters stage area bringing paraphernalia to make a circus. She pushes a full length mirror on wheels. She is brash and sexy. With gawdy awning she lays out a circus ring and puts up flags and banners, singing snippits of a pop song, wagging her hips as she works and takes stock of her work. She chews gum. Snaps fingers. Does a few dance steps. The acting area is festive for a circus.

Enter Cornelius. He stands watching the Girl. She feels his eyes on her. Girl reacts to Cornelius the male.

Girl: Well, hi there sweetie.

Cornelius: Say, do you know if there's any work round here—any jobs?

Girl: Work for you baby? Bet we could sure find a job for you, if you'd like to hang around here. D'you think, sweetie, that you'd like to hang around here, uum?

Cornelius: Sure. I need a job.

Girl: Any good as a clown?

Cornelius: Me? What me? A clown?

Girl: Thought you said you wanted a job.

Cornelius: Yeah, but a clown! I couldn't do that.

Girl: Aach. Nothing to it sweetie. Anybody can be a clown for kids. In a God-forsaken little dump of a town like this, who cares? If you won't do it, then I'll have to be the clown. Circus got to have a clown. *Does a pointedly clumsy somersault, making funny faces. She fools around clowning, wagging her hips.*

If you be the clown, then I can be the beautiful lady on the white horse. *Pirouettes, then poses on one leg in a sort of arabesque.*

Cornelius: Does your circus have a white horse? Or a black horse with a silver mane? Or a white horse?

Girl: Are you kidding? Kid you're a laugh. You're naive. This is just kid stuff. You don't need anything real for kids, don't you know that? No we don't got a horse. We got a big truck. And we got this lion in a cage. An old thing. We have to prod the old bag of rags to make him open his eyes. He's so dead and dopey we got a roar for him on a tape recorder. Listen to this—eh.

Girl sets tape recorder going. Sound of loud and splendid roars. The tape recorder now continues to let out lion roars to punctuate the rest of the circus scene.

Isn't that wild. I ask you. Come on kiddo, say yes. It isn't so bad. We can have us wild times, you and me.

Say yes, yes, yes. Say yes and you'll be the clown in the circus. Clown, clown, in the greatest show on earth. Roll up, roll up, see the clown in the greatest show on earth—

Cornelius: Okay. I'll give it a try. You'll have to show me what to do.

You will show me what to do, won't you?

Girl: You'll be fine. Sure I'll show you, but who ever has to show a guy how to be a clown—just comes naturally.

Here, get into this— *Collects clown suit from clothes tree and spreads it out for Cornelius.* A clown suit fits anybody, all one size.

Get with it. Get into it. Got to hurry before the kids start coming.

You get into the clown while I—I—shall make myself into the beautiful, the scintillating—the captivating—most beautiful— lady.

Girl faces Cornelius and whips off her T-shirt. Cornelius' mouth drops open. Half embarrassed but mesmerized he keeps his eyes on her as he steps into his clown suit.

Cornelius: Beautiful lady—on a white horse.

Girl slips off her jeans and is a dancer in skin pink. She talks as she collects circus outfit of glittering tutu, sequined bra, blonde wig, large eyelashes, lipstick. She dances to bemuse Cornelius.

Girl: I'll do you up. You do me up.

Girl slips into her tutu, pirouettes to tease, arranges ruffles round the clown's neck. Mimes approval. Turn him round and round making a big show of doing him up. She slips into her sequined bra and turns for him to fasten it.

Do me up.

Before Cornelius can do her up she spins away, then turns to face him.

Say kid, what's your name?

Cornelius: Jim. Jim Black. What's yours?

Girl: Blondie. Blondie the beautiful. Here, do me up Jimbo. *Turns for the clown to do her up, mock bows as he fastens her bra, spreading her arms with exaggeration.*

Jimbo the clown and Blondie the beautiful. Ladies and Gentlemen—that's us. *Spins over to mirror and preening, puts on the wig.*

Cornelius: You sure are beautiful—Blondie.

Girl: Thanks Jimbo. Hey, get me my slippers from over there. Get your feet on too.

Cornelius clowns to prop rack to collect feet. Clowns over to girl, her slippers in one hand, attacking his feet in the other hand, in a clumsy boxing match. Cornelius pulls his head both ways, making himself both sides of the audience in his fight show. Meanwhile Girl is putting on eyelashes and lipstick.

Cornelius makes a clowning business of putting on his feet. Falls, rolls over backwards. Clowns for Girl then for himself in the mirror.

Girl: Jimbo. You need your nose.

Cornelius clowns to collect his nose. He puts it on behind her while she is at the mirror. He puts his hands on her waist, and they do a clown dance with him reaching from the back to kiss her loudly on both cheeks.

Jimbo. Jimbo, you need your balloons. Hey, Bill. Can you hear? We got a clown. Bring in the balloons.

A bunch of balloons is handed in. Cornelius dances with them, almost lyrically.

There, there, you're a proper clown now. Just like in a kid's colouring book. Perfect.

Cornelius and Girl look at each other, making mirror images of each other's expressions and movements, playing the mirror game with each other. Finally they bow to themselves.

Girl: Okay Jimbo.

Cornelius: Okay Blondie. Hope I know what to do.

Girl: Just do what comes naturally, Jimbo. As I told you before, every guy I've ever known knew how to be a clown.

Cornelius is flattered. Does somersaults, yapping like a puppy dog.

Girl: Hey, Bill. We're all ready in here. Let 'em come in.

Bill nonchalant. Puts on top hat. Assumes character of show-biz ringmaster. Collects whip. Flicks and snaps it. Guides the children in.

Here we go. Ready Jimbo. Strike up the band.

Girl snaps fingers, turns on tape-recorded music. The lion still roars. Girl puts on big smile and poses to welcome the children. Jimbo imitates her. They bow and bow. Make as though great crowds are gathering. Bill cracks his whip.

Bill: Roll in. Roll in. Fill up the seats. Come on in ladies and gentlemen, lads and lassies, lords and ladies. Come and be happy—come and have fun.

Stagehand carries in masks on poles as used before. He holds them low because they are little children. He places himself and them at the front of real audience.

That's right, take your seats. Sit down there and smile. Let's see those great big happy smiles. Are we happy?

All: Yes, we're happy—happy—

Bill: Are we happy? Louder. Let me hear you.

All: Yes. Happy—happy—

Cornelius cartwheels, balloons and all. Girl pirouettes energetically. Lion roars. Music booms. Whip cracks.

Bill: Are we ready for the greatest show on earth? No wait, wait. Here comes another one.

In comes a figure completely covered in a shapeless drab coat and a felt hat pulled down over its eyes, its feet in sloppy rubber boots. It shuffles in and takes its place in the front row. Cornelius and Girl mime mockery of the newcomer.

Girl: You got to be kidding.

Cornelius: You got to be kidding.

Bill dances flipping and snapping his whip at Blondie who makes like she's on a white horse circling the ring. Clown lies on floor, a centerpiece with balloons, clowning with crazy gestures with arms and legs. When Blondie finishes her turn, clown jumps up, applauds her, clapping and shouting.

Cornelius: Bravo, bravo. Beautiful lady. Beautiful white horse.

Now Cornelius takes off round the circle in imitation of Blondie, but he tries to be the horse and the dancer. He whinnies. When Cornelius whinnies Blondie pirouettes.

Girl: Jimbo   Jimbo   Jimbo.

Clown and Blondie co-operate in a dance. She performs as a ballet dancer and he makes clownish imitations. They make like swans then lovers. She teases him. He catches her by the back of her bra and makes her dance backwards. He falls. She gets away. He catches her again round the waist. They dance grotesquely together. He treads on her toes. She smacks him. He tips her up, lifts her skirt and paddles her behind. Then they dance again. End with a kiss, an arabesque, a somersault. They bow to each other, to the audience.

Girl: See you all again, kids.

Cornelius: Bye, bye, going now.

Girl: Goodbye, goodbye, be seeing you.

Cornelius: Boobye . . . boobye . . . booooo . . .

Cornelius and Girl leave waving and bowing.

Stagehand walks the masks out. The music stops. The lion roars. The covered person sits. Bill removes top hat, puts on janitor cap, and begins sweeping the ring.

Cornelius and Girl come back on. Girl flops exhausted onto the ground, pulls off her wig and chews her gum.

Bill: Switch that damn lion off willya.

Cornelius roars like a lion, makes like a lion. Switches off the tape but roars again himself.

Person: Ha, ha, ha, ha—

Girl, Bill, Cornelius focus attention on the Person, suddenly noticing her.

Girl: Hey you kid. Whatcha think you're doing here. Circus over. Git. Vamoose.

Person: I want to talk to the clown.

Girl: No kidding. Be realistic willya. Off you go—

Person: I want to talk to the clown.

Bill: Show's over kid. Time to move on. What are you anyhow? Can't tell if you're a boy or a girl.

Girl: What's it matter to you buster, whether it's a boy or a girl, eh? Got plans, have ya?

Person: I want to talk to the clown.

Girl: For crying out loud. Can't you say anything else? I want to talk to the clown. I want to talk to the clown. Are you stupid or something?

Person: I want to talk to the clown.

Girl: Well, I can't take any more of this. Come on youse guys, let's throw it out of here.

Girl, Cornelius, Bill advance on Person.

Girl: If you don't move right sharp kid, we're going to sling you out like a dead cat. One - two - three -

Person: I want to talk to the clown.

Girl: Grab. Get it.

Person practices passive resistance as it is ejected.

Out - out - out.

Person: I want to talk to the clown.

Girl: Good riddance. Don't know how a kid could get that crazy. Stupid. Whew. I'm going to rest up a bit after that. Seeya Bill. Seeya Jimbo—next show—

Bill: I'll be leaving too. Be seeing you Jimbo. You did real good, kid. Be seein' ya.

Bill and Girl leave. Cornelius stands alone posed as a forlorn clown holding his balloons. Thinks about hanging his balloons up but goes to window with them in his hand. Goes outside the window to look in on the circus scene and the audience. Clowning he comes to inside to look out. Hangs balloons up; in so doing he touches the wind chime, like a memory, listens. Touches it again more firmly. Listening, he pushes his false nose up on his forehead, sits down to loosen his false feet. Half Cornelius, half clown.

The Person crawls in under the edge of the circus circle, carrying its rubber boots. It is barefooted. Hands and feet are the only parts of Person showing. Cornelius does not see it. Person crawls around until it is able to face him.

Person: Hi.

Cornelius startled. Pulls his false nose back into place. Jumps up and towers over the Person.

Person: Hi.

Cornelius: What do you want?

Person: I want to talk to the clown.

Cornelius: Are you crazy or something?

Person: Crazy? Clowns are crazy, aren't they. Fools.

Cornelius: Well, what do you think you are? In disguise, eh?

Person: You're in disguise, aren't you?

Cornelius: I'm a clown.

Person: So! I'm a nobody.

Cornelius: Everybody's somebody.

Person: Umph. Are you really a clown?

Cornelius: Are you really a nobody?

Person: Do you have a name?

Cornelius: Jimbo the clown. *Clowns, standing on his hands.*

Person: Are you a clown inside that thing?

Cornelius: Are you a nobody inside that thing? Do you have a name?

Person: Nitty the nobody.

Cornelius: That's not a name.

Person: As much as Jimbo the clown, it is.

Cornelius: So.

Person: So.

Cornelius: *Sits down facing Person.* So.

Person: Your feet are ridiculous.

Cornelius: At least I can take them off. Yours are naked. *Takes his false feet off. Clowning.*

Person: So.

Cornelius: It's indecent to go about naked. Dangerous.

Cornelius makes his feet naked. He shuffles to make his naked feet face the naked feet of Person. Person shuffles until the two pairs of feet at the end of straight legs are exactly facing but not touching.

Person: Are you naked inside that . . . costume?

Cornelius: *Clowns embarrassment, horror, indignation.* That's a very personal question. Are you naked inside that . . . costume?

Person: That's a very personal question. Naked hands. *Puts up the flats of its hands to face Cornelius.*

Cornelius: Ooooow-hands naked. Feel naked-ooow.

Cornelius kneels up to Person and puts his hands to touch hers. They both kneel up and play handclapping game like children.

Person/Cornelius: Pat-a-cake, pat-a-cake, pat-a-cake, pat-a-cake -

Cornelius: Touch, touch.

Person: Touch if you can.

Cornelius/Person: Touch-touch-touch.

Person: Clown-fool-jester-idiot.

Cornelius: Man

Cornelius/Person: Pat-a-cake, pat-a-cake. Touch, if you can.

Cornelius: Nobody . . somebody. In disguise, hide your eyes.

Cornelius/Person: Touch. Touch if you can. Touch . . . touch . . . touch. Touch.

Cornelius and Person pause with hands pressed together.

Person: Touch the hands—can touch the heart.

Cornelius and Person jump away from each other as though burned. They stand facing each other with their hands behind them.

Why don't you take that silly nose off?

Cornelius: Why don't you take that silly hat off?

Person/Cornelius: I will if you will.

Cornelius and Person watch each other carefully. He pushes his nose up on his head. Person pushes hat up on head revealing face and eyes.

Cornelius: Hey there—you're a girl. What's your name?

Person: What's your name?

Cornelius: Jim Black.

Person: What a dull, unimaginative name.

Cornelius: Then what's your name?

Person: Arathusa Zeigleman.

Cornelius: You got to be kidding. You got to be kidding.

Person: *Pulls her hat down over her face again. Cries angrily.* Clown . . . clown . . . fool . . . jester . . . idiot . . . fool.

Cornelius snatches off his nose and hat. Grabs Person, pulls off her hat, turns her round. Person covers her face with her hands looking at Cornelius through her fingers.

Cornelius: Arathusa Zeigleman, listen to this, will you. My real name is Cornelius Horatio Dragon.

Person: You've got to be kidding—you've got to be kidding—

Cornelius: Arathusa Zeigleman.

Person: Cornelius Horatio Dragon.

Cornelius and Person become embarrassed, laugh, turn away from each other. She puts her hands over her face, he does a little clown swaggering.

Girl comes in chewing, sexy, Blondie wig in hand.

Girl: Hey you, kid, what're you doing here? I thought we threw you out.

Person: I'm talking to the clown.

Girl: Hey Jimbo, why didn't you kick it out? Want some help? Here, give it a good shove.

Cornelius: Leave her alone. She isn't doing any harm.

Girl: Ah, it's a her is it? What's wrong with you Jimbo? Getting soft? Do you want to wreck the circus? Letting a silly kid see you without your face on.

Cornelius: She's not a silly kid. She's . . . she's . . .

Girl: Sure as hell doesn't look like anybody to me. Are you sure it's a girl inside that thing? That screwy thing it's wearing?

Cornelius: Leave her alone, will you.

Bill enters in janitor's cap but cracks his ringmaster's whip.

Bill: What's all the shouting? What's going on in here? Hey you. Get out. I thought we threw you out. Get out. We don't let kids see behind the circus.

Person: You're scared . . . that's all.

Bill: Scared. I'll show you who's scared.

Girl takes Person by scruff and shakes.

Cornelius: Leave her alone will you. She's not doing any harm.

Girl: She's made a fool out of you. You should never show anybody behind the circus.

Bill: Throw her out.

Cornelius: If she goes, I go.

Girl and Bill stare at Cornelius. Girl has Person by the scruff.

Bill: You can't go. We need a clown.

Girl: That's right. We need a clown.

Cornelius: Anybody can be a clown.

Person: Anyhow, he's not really a clown inside.

Girl: *Shakes Person to punctuate her words.* What do you know about clowns? You, you—what d'you think you know about clowns?

Person: I was talking to the clown.

Girl: You, you have no right to be talking to our clown.

Bill: Let's get her out of here before she sees everything.

Cornelius: Then I'm not staying. *Takes off clown costume.*

Girl: What else do you think you can do, Jim Black. You got no choice.

Person: He can go back home.

Cornelius: Hey . . . Arathusa, how did you know to say that?

Person: I guessed you have a home. I have a home. I was running away, Cornelius.

Girl: Arathusa! What a freak. Just look at you. *Lets go Person, stands back to survey her contemptuously.* Got a place for a thing like this in a sideshow, Bill?

Bill: Cornelius . . . Jeeze . . . takes one to know one. A freak to find a freak. You weren't much good as a clown anyhow. Good riddance.

Person looks at Cornelius without his disguise. She undoes her coat, slips it off and lets it drop. Person is wearing strikingly pretty, strongly coloured clothes. She tosses her head and looks lovely. Cornelius shakes his head, smiles, stands up straight. Girl and Bill take an ugly, mocking stance together, watching as Cornelius and Person walk out, hand in hand, through audience.

Stinking rotten luck—wouldn't you know it. Now we've got to look for another clown for the next show.

Girl: That one wasn't much good anyhow. Plenty more where he came from. There's always some freak kid who comes along and spoils everything. Spoils our show.

Bill: Yah. Remember that one what kept yelling, That's not a real lion—

Girl: And that one who screamed at me Why don't you get a white horse?

Bill: Kids, kids. Know too much for their own good these days.

Girl: No sense of magic.

Bill: Too much TV.

Girl: Kills you, don't it.

Bill: Well, come on Blondie. Better start looking for another clown. The show must go on.

Girl: There'll be one somewhere here.

Girl and Bill walk out through the audience scanning it for a clown.

Bill: Never have to look very hard.

Enter Cornelius, to take stance as at beginning of play. He sounds the wind chime as at beginning. Confides to audience as at beginning.

Cornelius: Hi. I am Cornelius Dragon. Cornelius Horatio Dragon, for that matter.

He points to props, discarded clothes. The other actors come in as themselves. Stage hand brings in the crowd masks. Cornelius acknowledges them all.

The actors. The masks. The props. The pretences—and me.

And I am Cornelius Dragon.

That's all.

Cornelius touches the wind chimes to gentle the end.

■

More of a Family
Alf Silver

*Debra Wiens, Randy Wood, and Cynthia Tymchuk from the 1978
Neighbourhood Theatre production.*

More of a Family was commissioned by The Neighbourhood Theatre in May, 1978. The play opened in full production at the Manitoba Theatre Workshop, October 12, 1978. The director was Deborah Quinn, Artistic Director of The Neighbourhood Theatre, with settings and lights designed by Shawn Kimelman. The original cast was as follows:

Amy ————————————————————— Debra Wiens

Tony, Mr. Pirelli, ————————————————— David Gillies
George, Barney,
Ben, Fred

Joey, Kevin, ——————————————— Randy Wood
Bobby, Gregor

Louise, Ellen, ——————————— Cynthia Tymchuk
Christine, Mrs. Gregor

Mrs. Pirelli, Mrs. Hamlin, ——————— Rebecca Toolan
Irma, Janice, Mrs. Vogel,
Teresa

The setting is Winnipeg's West End, a multi-cultural neighbourhood. The present.

Requests for performance rights should be addressed to:

Alf Silver
Manitoba Theatre Centre
174 Market Street
Winnipeg, Manitoba
Canada   R3B 0P8

Amy's mother's apartment, slightly cluttered, with many school books and papers. Amy comes on as the audience is being seated. Amy is eleven years old. She's dressed in blue jeans and a T-shirt and has Adidas on her feet. She is packing her suitcase (which has wheels) and writing the letter. Sound of inane family sit-com from T.V. Amy exits. Comes back with baseball glove which she packs in the suitcase, closes suitcase, shuts off T.V. and sits to finish letter.

Amy: *Writing.* "I think you've given a good try at raising a daughter all by yourself, but I think I need more of a family. I'll come back to visit you," especially when you make lasagna, "so don't worry about me. Goodbye. Yours truly, Amelia Hebinski." *Reading over what she has written.* "Mizz Teresa O'Connel, 36-992 Wolseley Avenue, Winnipeg, Manitoba T3G 1E9. To Whom It May Concern. This is your daughter Amy writing. I won't be here when you get home. That's because I don't think we can live together any more." I hope she doesn't take that personally. "Because I've decided I need a more normal environment to grow up in." It's not that there's anything bad about living here, except I wonder if I have to do too much housework? I betcha if Jane Crawford had to help her mom as much as me, she couldn't keep her marks up higher than mine. "I've got nothing against you as a mother, except sometimes I wish you would think a little bit more about me when you're picking your boyfriends." I used to think it'd be nice when she got a steady boyfriend and stopped introducing me to strange men, but why'd it have to be Fred? *Mimes Fred pinching her cheek.* "Hi, Snooks." Yuch. I'm a person too, you know. What does he think I am? The family dog? "I guess Fred's a good guy, but I hate it when he pinches my cheek and calls me Snooks. If I was a dog I'd bite off his thumbs. I think you've given a good try at raising a daughter all by yourself, but I think I need more of a family. I'll come back to visit you, so don't worry about me. Goodbye. Yours truly, Amelia Hebinski."

She seals the letter, goes to pick up suitcase—goes back to letter and opens it up again.

"P.S. I borrowed your suitcase. I hope you don't mind." *Reseals the letter with scotch tape,* I did leave the television set, and my dad gave it to me when he left—when they separated. Maybe I'll come back and get it sometime—and bring back the suitcase. *Picks up suitcase and moves downstage.* I wonder what my normal family will be like? I hope it has lots of kids. Louise Pirelli has a big family. An extra kid won't make much difference. Lots of brothers and sisters—it'll be like coming home to recess; no more trying to think of games to play by myself. Might take them a little while to get used to me, but then I'll be just like one of the family . . . *We hear chimes as Amy dreams.*

Amy's imagined versions of the Pirelli children bustle on, laughing, dribbling a soccer ball (mimed). They wear outsize caricature plaster heads. Louise is Amy's age. She wears a yellow dress and knee socks. Tony is slightly older; Joe is about seven. They all speak in excessively sweet television commercial tones. Joe tends to fall down a lot.

Joe: Oh boy! Our sister Amy's home from school.

Tony: I hope your science essay turned out better than snooty old Jane Crawford's.

Amy: Mrs. Thompson said mine was the best in the class.

Pirelli kids: Hooray!

Tony: Now that you're home we can play teams.

Louise: Sisters against brothers.

Joe: You gotta promise not to trip me and bump my head like last time.

Louise: I'd never hurt my little brother on purpose.

Joe: Aw, I guess you wouldn't.

Tony: Let's play catch.

Louise: And after we can play house.

Tony: I'll be the father.

Joe: And I'll be the baby. 'N our sister Amy can be the Mom.

They play catch a while, cheering at each successful catch of the ball. Then Amy's imagined Mrs. Pirelli enters, wearing an excessively sweet mask.

Mrs. Pirelli: Dinner's ready!

Children: Aw!

Mrs. Pirelli: We're having Shake 'n Bake.

Children: Yay!

Mrs. Pirelli: And for dessert there's Stir and Frost!

Children: Yay!

Mrs. Pirelli: You children are such a joy to cook for. *Exits.*

Tony: *As the children run inside.* We can play house after dinner.

Amy: *Still on; walking out of her daydream.* I can't understand why the girls at school are always complaining about their brothers.

Amy knocks at the Pirelli door. The real Pirelli children are watching TV. Louise wears the clothes of the daydream Louise, though her at-home manners belie the Pollyanna effect. Tony is on the verge of adolescence. He wears a brightly coloured disco shirt and jeans. Joey, at seven, is the baby and extremely clumsy. Mrs. Pirelli enters. Though her English is unaccented, she's still not totally comfortable with the language. She has an air of placid distraction.

Tony: Somebody's at the door.

Mrs. Pirelli: Yeah, yeah. You could answer it once in a while. *Answers the door.* Hello. Are you looking for Louise? She's in watching TV.

Amy: Thank you. *She walks by Mrs. Pirelli dragging her suitcase.*

Louise: Hi Amy. What's in the suitcase?

Amy: My clothes and things. I've come to live with you.

Louise: Why? Did your mom and you have a fight?

Amy: No, but I need a family to live with.

Louise: *Rising.* I guess you could live in Joe's room and Joe could move in with Tony.

Joe: No way. Tony never lets me make truck noises.

Tony: Shut up, Toad. This is the good part.

Amy: I don't mind sharing your room with you, Louise. It'll be fun.

Louise: Oh sure, lots of fun. I had to share it with my sister Angie all my life, until she finished school and moved out. She put up pictures of dumb singers all over everything so you couldn't hardly move, and she never let me play the radio and she talked on the phone all night so I couldn't sleep. Now I've finally got my own room I ain't going to share it.

Joe: Mom says don't say ain't.

Louise: You shut up, Warty.

Joe: Don't call me that.

Louise: Warty.

Joe: Just for that, I'm keeping my room. She's your friend, she can stay with you.

Louise: She will not.

Joe: Will too.

Louise: Will not! *Punches Joe's arm; he punches her back.* OW! Mom—he hit me!

Joe: She hit me first.

Louise: Not that hard, right Amy?

Joe: Was too. It's all bruises. You saw her hit me hard, didn't you?

Louise: It wasn't all that hard, was it?

Amy is saved from having to cope with the side-choosing, as Tony suddenly grabs Louise in a head-lock.

Tony: *Knuckling Louise's head.* There's Shaun Cassidy, Louise, isn't he cute?

Louise: OW!! MOM!!

Tony: *Letting her go.* Shh!! This is the good part.

Mrs. Pirelli: Dinner's ready.

Tony: *Jumping up.* I gotta go, Mom. I promised Jerry I'd help push his car into the garage. I'll get a hot dog.

Mrs. Pirelli: I'll put something in the fridge for you. *Tony is gone.*

Louise: What's for dinner?

Mrs. Pirelli: Chicken.

Joe: Blecch. I hate chicken.

Louise: You do not.

Joe: Do too.

Louise: Amy's going to stay here Mom.

Mrs. Pirelli: Did you phone your mother, Amy?

Amy: She's not expecting me home.

Mrs. Pirelli: All right then, there's plenty of food. *Calling out back door.* Joe! *To Amy.* Here, pass me your plate, dear. *Begins dishing out chicken to Amy as others load up.* Joe! Supper's ready.

Mr. Pirelli: *Enters. He is not a man of violent temper. He's tired after his day at work and is accustomed to having his way at home.* All right. Hey, aren't we forgetting something?

Amy: What? *Everyone has removed hands from table. Mr. Pirelli sits at head of the table, says a quick grace and crosses himself.*

Mrs. Pirelli: Pass your plate, please Joey. *Loads on chicken.*

Joe: My name's Joe—Dad?

Mr. Pirelli: Don't talk back to your mother. Pass the bread.

Louise: Could I have some milk, please?

Mrs. Pirelli: Would you like some too, dear?

Amy: Please.

Mrs. Pirelli: Don't use so much salt, Joey, you'll get lumps in your throat.

Amy: In school today . . .

Joe: Pass the potatoes.

Mrs. Pirelli: Say please.

Joe: Please. *Louise passes the potatoes.*

Mrs. Pirelli: Eat your peas, Joey.

Joe: I hate peas.

Mr. Pirelli: EAT! *Joe does so.* Pass the potatoes.

Amy: In school today I drew a . . .

Louise: Could I have more chicken, please?

Mrs. Pirelli: Pass your plate, dear.

Mr. Pirelli: Those are peas, Joey, they're not little soccer balls. They belong on your plate or in your stomach, not on the floor.

Amy: I drew a picture that Mrs. Thompson said was the best picture of a cat she'd ever seen in a grade six art class.

Louise: Pass the milk.

Mrs. Pirelli: Say please, Louise.

Joe: Please, Louise, say please Louise, eat your peas, Louise.

Louise: Shut UP!

Mrs. Pirelli: Don't fight at the table.

All continue, volume rising—ad lib.

Mr. Pirelli: That was good, thank you. All right—*All quiet.* You kids help your mother with the dishes. *Gets up and moves to TV.*

Mrs. Pirelli: You can go in and watch TV. with Mr. Pirelli, Amy. We'll clear the dishes.

As Amy goes to the living room, the kids begin taking dishes to the kitchen.

Joe: *Off, following loud crash.* I dropped one.

Mrs. Pirelli: Oh, Joey, you know not to carry so many at once.

Amy joins Mr. Pirelli who is gazing at the tube, sipping a glass of wine and smoking.

Amy: *After a pause.* What's on?

Mr. Pirelli: *Not looking from set.* Kojak.

Amy: The Muppets are on, too. Wouldn't you rather watch the Muppets?

The outrageousness of the suggestion pulls Pirelli away from the set to stare at her, then the sound of gunshots and sirens rivets his attention back to it.

Amy: Do you work? *No response.* My mom goes to university, do you go to university?

Mr. Pirelli: *Showing grease-caked fingernails.* Does that look like I go to university? You find someone else to pay the mortgages and buy the groceries, and I'll go to university. *Louise enters.* Why aren't you helping your mother with the dishes?

Louise: She said I should come in here so my guest will feel comfortable. *Sits by Amy.*

Amy: We can walk to school together tomorrow.

Louise: I guess so.

Amy: *To Mr. Pirelli.* Where do you work? *No response.* Where does your father work?

Louise: In a garage. He fixes transmissions.

Amy: What's a transmission?

Mr. Pirelli: SShh!

Mrs. Pirelli and Joey enter and sit, Joe on the floor, Mrs. Pirelli on arm of Mr. Pirelli's chair.

Amy: Let's go outside and play.

Louise: Play what?

Amy: We could play catch. Or we could play house, and Joey could be the father.

Joe: Girls play house.

Louise: I wouldn't play with Joey if you paid me.

Mr. Pirelli: SSHH!

Joe: What else is on?

Amy: The Muppets.

Joe: What channel? *Makes a move towards the TV.*

Mr. Pirelli: Joey, do you like to sit?

Joe: I guess so, Dad.

Mr. Pirelli: If you touch that dial you won't be able to sit for a week.

Amy: Your father's mean.

Louise: He is not. You can't say that.

Joe: She can too.

Louise: You don't even know what she said.

Joe: Do too.

Louise: What did she say?

Joe: I don't have to tell you.

Mr. Pirelli: Quiet. This is the good part.

Joe: All right. If you're so smart, what did she say?

Louise: You don't even know.

Joe: Do too.

Louise: Do not.

Joe: Do too.

Louise: Do not, Warty.

Joe: Don't call me that.

Mr. Pirelli: SHUT UP!

Amy: *Softly, to Mrs. Pirelli.* How can you stand it with all this noise all the time?

Mrs. Pirelli: What noise? *Amy begins exiting with suitcase, noise suddenly subsides.*

Mr. Pirelli: How come you kids are always quiet when the commercials are on? I don't want to hear the commercials. Ah. *Show starts again.*

Mrs. Pirelli: *Gasps at something happening on TV.*

Mr. Pirelli: What's wrong?

Mrs. Pirelli: What they do to each other . . .

Mr. Pirelli: It's just a show, nobody really gets hurt.

Amy walks away from the Pirellis, thinking aloud as she goes.

Amy: That's not what I thought a normal family was like. Maybe they're not normal. There's Kevin Hamlin's house—Kevin Gremlin. He's not really a gremlin. He's just shy—maybe because he's an only child. He'd probably be happy to have a sister. *She knocks on the door. Mrs. Hamlin answers.*

Amy: Hello Mrs. Gremlin, I mean Mrs. Hamlin. Is Kevin home?

Mrs. Hamlin: He's in the rec. room playing with his chemistry set. I could get him for you.

Amy: It's all right. I'll find him. *Walking past her.* Where's the rec. room?

Mrs. Hamlin: Just through the kitchen.

Amy: Okay. Don't bother to show me. I'll have to learn to find my way around by myself anyway.

Amy walks off leaving a befuddled Mrs. Hamlin to close the door. Kevin is sitting on the floor with bubbling test tubes all round him.

Amy: Kevin?

Kevin: *Peering through smoke and steamed glasses.* Who's there?

Amy: Amy Hebinski.

Kevin: Who? Oh, third row, fourth desk. What are you doing here?

Amy: I've come to live with you.

Kevin: Why? Did your house burn down?

Amy: I don't live in a house; I live—lived in an apartment.

Kevin: Did the apartment block burn down? That's even better.

Amy: No. I just decided me and my mom weren't enough of a family. I thought maybe you'd like to have a sister, too, so you wouldn't be lonely.

Kevin: Lonely? I'm not lonely. I've got my experiments to keep me busy and when I'm tired of them I play my electric guitar or listen to my stereo or target shoot with my pellet gun.

Amy: Your parents must be rich.

Kevin: Hardly. Harry writes for the Trib and Beth works at the Cornish Library. What's the use of having an intelligent kid if they don't invest in him? Are your parents divorced?

Amy: Just separated. My mom says they'll be divorced soon.

Kevin: It must be fun. I bet you get to play them back and forth and get all kinds of neat stuff.

Amy: I never thought of that.

Kevin: You won't be able to get much here except the stuff I'm tired of. You could help me with my experiments, though. That'd be fun.

Amy: What kind of experiments?

Kevin: I'm trying to come up with a reliable explosive you carry in your pocket. It has to be pretty stable or if you slipped on the ice in the winter and fell down, you'd blow your leg off; but simple enough to detonate with a fuse so you could just rip off a chunk quick while you're walking by a teacher's desk, stick on a fuse from your other pocket, and leave her a nice surprise. You could use bigger chunks for busses when bus drivers make fun of you for not having the right change. And smaller ones for dogs that bark at you, and great big ones for stores downtown that yell at you for looking at their magazines or stare at you like you're trying to steal something. I sent a letter to the Minister of Defence for the plastique formula but he never wrote back. So I guess I'll have to invent something. I'm also trying to invent a poison that won't kill people, just turn their skin green and make their hair fall out.

Mrs. Hamlin: *Entering with tray.* I thought you and your little friend might like some milk and cookies, Kevin.

Amy: I'm going now. *Quickly exits.*

Mrs. Hamlin: What a strange little girl. Why is she pulling that suitcase around?

Kevin: *Munching cookie.* Her apartment burnt down and her mother was fried to a crisp so she's looking for a place to live. *Surreptitiously pours contents of test tube into the second milk glass.*

Mrs. Hamlin: You shouldn't make up stories like that, dear.

Kevin: Would you like a glass of milk?

Mrs. Hamlin: No thank you, dear. You know I never drink milk. I have to clean up the supper dishes. *Exits.*

Kevin: Kitty, here kitty, kitty. *Exiting with glass of milk held out enticingly.* I've got a nice treat for you. Where are you kitty?

Amy: I wonder why Kevin wants to blow up Mrs. Thompson? He seems to like being an only child. Maybe he's weird because he is an only child. Maybe I seem weird to other people too. No. I'm okay. I don't want to blow up Eatons or the Bay.

I guess having no brothers and sisters isn't so bad if you've got both your parents living with you. If Mom didn't have to look after me and go to university too, I wouldn't have to help so much and be responsible. Two parents living together wouldn't have to go out so much either, and leave me alone with baby sitters, 'cause they wouldn't get lonely like a mother alone does. They'd both be around a lot more with nothing to worry about but me . . . *Chimes.*

Irma bustles on, a daydream caricature of a sweet, well kept-up modern matron with a smiling mask.

Irma: Are you home from school already, Amy? And the chocolate pudding isn't set yet. *Drawing up chair.* You sit down and I'll get you a glass of chocolate milk while you're waiting.

Amy: But Irma, won't that spoil my appetite?

Irma: Not a growing girl like you. George, our Amy's home. *Exits.*

George: *Ditto version of sweet old man, though slightly scruffy.* At last, I get so lonely here when she's at school. Amy? Are you comfortable, would you like a pillow?

Amy: *As George sets cushion behind her head.* I drew a picture in Art class that Mrs. Thompson said was the best picture of a cat she'd ever seen in a grade six art class.

George: Boy, you're so talented and intelligent, it really makes me proud, almost like I was your real father.

Amy: And Miss Gavin made fun of me in Phys. Ed. when I couldn't climb the rope.

George: I'll march right down to the school tomorrow and speak to the principal.

Irma: *Enters with ornate, tall glass of chocolate milk.* I heard that about the drawing. George, do you think we can afford to send Amy to that art school they have to teach talented young artists?

George: I will just have to get a night job.

Irma: And I'll work weekends.

George: And we can sell the car.

Irma: But then Amy will have to walk to school, and you know how tired she gets.

George: Then we'll just sell this house and buy another one closer to her school. What do you think of that idea, Amy?

Amy: I think I'd rather be the first woman major-league baseball player. They're starting to play me in left field now. I like it better than first base, but that infielder's glove I got is too small. I saw a glove in the window of the hardware store that was a real outfielder's glove. It was ace.

George suddenly exits.

Irma: What would you like for dinner, dear?

Amy: *As Irma writes it down like a waitress.* Lasagne, and Chinese salad, and uh, jello and ice cream mixed together, and, uh, apple pie for dessert. Oh, and strawberry Quick to drink.

Irma bustles off, as George runs on, panting.

George: *Holding his hands behind his back.* Pick a hand, Amy. *She does so.* Ta da!! *New fielder's glove—gives it to Amy.* Is that the one you wanted?

Amy: That's it all right.

George: You like it?

Amy: I guess so. Needs breaking in, though.

George: I'll stay up all night throwing a ball into it to wear in the pocket. If you want anything, just holler. *Exits, working on the glove.*

Amy: I will. *Thinking aloud.* George and Irma don't have any kids, and they're always super nice to us when they see us going to school. I bet they'd be happy to have a daughter.

The real Irma is tending roses in her front yard. She has a fairly strong German accent.

Hi Irma.

Irma: Hm? Oh, Amy, how nice of you to come by and say hello.

Amy: I came to say more than hello. I've come to live with you and George.

Irma: What happened to your mother?

Amy: Nothing. I just decided I needed more of a family.

Irma: And you thought George and I would be a nice family for you. How sweet. Come inside and I'll phone your mama.

Amy: You don't have to do that, she knows I won't be home.

Irma: Of course I do. Come inside.

They go in. George is working on the innards of the TV set. He is very energetic for a middle-aged man. He's puffing an unlit cigar.

Irma: George . . .

George: Yes, my sweet, what is it?

Irma: Amy has come to stay with us for a while. Could you make room for her to sleep in the den until I clean out the storage room?

George: I'll see. *Takes measuring tape and approaches Amy. He measures her width and height.* Yup. There's room for you. But you'll have to sleep standing on your head. *Laughs.*

Irma: I'll phone your mama, you sit down, Amy. *Exits. Amy starts to sit.*

George: Don't sit there! You'll get slivers in your butt. Sit here. I should sand that down. *Fetching tool box.* So, uh—you play the horses?

Amy: No. I play baseball.

George: That's illegal.

Amy: It is not.

George: Betting on baseball? Sure is.

Amy: I mean I play baseball. *Mimes catching a fly ball.*

George: You're kidding. Girls playing baseball?

Amy: Sure.

George: Where I grew up, on the farm, girls never played baseball.

Amy: What did they do?

George: Hung around waiting for somebody to marry them. Never caught me.

Amy: Irma did.

George: Naw, not the same thing. I just came to fix her windows, and stayed, and I'm still fixing. *Laughs.*

Amy: Could I help you? *George has opened tool box and is kneeling by chair.*

George: Sure. *Hands out like a surgeon.* Sandpaper, two gauge. *Amy guesses, hands him a piece.* No, that's zero gauge, too light. The higher the number, the rougher the sandpaper is, you see what I mean? You need something heavier to wear down these ridges before smoothing it out with the light stuff. *Amy has taken back zero gauge and handed him two.* Thanks. *Goes to work.*

Amy: I like sanding.

George: So do I. You take something rough, work on it for a while, and then it's smooth. Now that's fun . . . There. Now that's smooth. Smooth as a baby's bum. *Amy chuckles.* I had a friend used to say that. Me and him used to play the horses all the time, out at Polo Park. *Packs tools.*

Amy: The shopping centre?

George: No, it used to be a racetrack before they put up the shopping centre. That's why it's called Polo Park, they used to play polo out there. Didn't you know that?

Amy: No.

George: Won a lot of money out there. Should have quit then, but I kept on playing. Lost it all. People are never satisfied with what they have. Always want more, something different from what they got. We're happy now—got this nice little house.

Irma: *Comes back on with dress and shoes.* Your mama wasn't home, Amy. But look what I found. I made this dress for my niece a few years ago, only she grew so fast she was too big before I finished it. Let's try it on you. George, did you make up a bed for Amy in your den?

George: Just going to do that right now. *Exits. Irma pulls the dress over Amy's head, begins fastening buttons.*

Irma: There. Now you look more like a little lady.

Amy: My mom says you don't have to wear a dress to be a lady.

Irma: *Working on Amy's hair.* That's true dear. There is so much more to it, deportment and grace and culture. That dress will be perfect for ballet classes.

Amy: Ballet?

Irma: It is very good for the grace and the posture, yes? And it makes you have so much more appreciation when you go to see the ballet.

Amy: It sounds kind of interesting, but I've always been more interested in athletic stuff.

Irma: My dear, there is nothing more athletic than the ballet.

Amy: Really?

Irma: I don't think even hockey players have to be in as good physical condition as ballet dancers. There, you look so lovely with your hair set like that. Now try these on. *Black patent pumps.*

Amy: You mean I have to take off my Adidas?

Irma: But of course. *She helps Amy put on shoes.* Then there's piano lessons, and deportment class and perhaps you should be enrolled in a French tutor's class.

George: *Entering.* Stand up a minute. *Measures from her waist to the floor.* Right about there.

Amy: What's right about there?

George: The counter for the stove and fridge and kitchen sink in the playhouse I'm going to build for you to play with. You don't want your kitchen stuff down around your knees or up over your head do you?

Amy: I'd rather have a spaceship.

George: Isn't that just like a female? Offer her a modern kitchen and she wants a spaceship. Tell you what—how about if I build you a space kitchen—with "closed-in counters of the third kind?" *Laughs as he exits.*

Irma: Would you like me to get you a nice glass of hot milk?

Amy: I don't like hot milk.

Irma: Of course you do, dear. All children like a glass of hot milk before bedtime.

Amy: Bedtime? It's only seven o'clock.

Irma: You can tell time on your own. My what a clever girl we are.

Amy: I'm going to be in Junior High next year. I'm not a baby.

Amy, standing on a chair, sees herself in the mirror all gussied up. As Irma speaks, Amy studies her reflection, then sits down and starts removing shoes.

Irma: Of course you're not, dear. But you can be our baby. Be a child as long as you can. At my age you can't be a child any more. Unless you have someone like George around. Why did you take off your shoes?

Amy: I don't feel comfortable in shoes I can't run in.

Irma: Young ladies don't run, dear. Except in gymnasiums.

Amy: Irma, I don't have time for music and ballet and deportment. I've got baseball, and then soccer and hockey, and all my schoolwork—I have to keep my marks up or I'll never get past Jane Crawford. I'm second highest in my class.

Irma: Young ladies shouldn't do *too* well in school. They scare the boys away. You're just going through what they call the tomboy stage; you'll grow out of it in a week or two.

Amy: I don't think so. *Removing hair ribbon and letting down hair.* Irma, you and George are nice people but I can't live with you. *Amy tries undoing buttons on back of dress, can't reach, Irma undoes them.*

Irma: But why?

Amy: I really like you and I'll come back and visit you, but I don't think I'm the right girl for you. You'd like a girl like Jane Crawford. *Dress is undone. She slips it off.* Thanks for letting me try on the dress.

Irma: You keep it. And the shoes too. Perhaps sometime you won't want to run. Put them in your suitcase.

Amy: But you can't just give them to me.

Irma: They're mine. I can do what I want with them. *Irma has placed shoes and dress in the suitcase, but has trouble closing one clasp.* The catch is broken. George could fix it for you.

Amy: Maybe another time. I'd better go now. Bye. *Exits.*

George: *Entering.* Where's Amy gone?

Irma: *Staring at empty chair.* For a moment I thought I was going to have a little girl of my own for a while.

George: But you're still stuck with nobody but me.

Irma: So why should I feel sorry for myself?

George holds tape measure up to Irma's face, checks measurement.

Irma: What are you doing?

George: Boy, is your face ever long. *She laughs.*

Irma: Come, I'll help you unmake the bed you made up for Amy. *They go off.*

Amy wanders into the park, sits down on a bench.

Amy: What am I going to do now? I've tried a big family and a small family and being an only child. Everything—except just living with a father. Can't do that with my own dad since he moved in with Helen and her kids. Don't know how he can stand it with them always playing those stupid word games. Probably just living with a father isn't any more normal than just with my mom. It sure is getting dark quick. *Opening suitcase.* I wonder if all my stuff's all right. All my wordly possessions. I wonder what exactly that's supposed to mean? *Taking out a book.* I wonder if anybody'd like me to read to them? *Seeing no likely prospects, she replaces the book and takes out a locket.* And the locket my dad gave me. He said it's real silver. I usually save it for special . . . *Trying it on, can't get clasp to catch.* My hair keeps getting in the way . . . *Brings clasp around in front of her face.* My mom usually fastens it for me. *Still can't get clasp to hold, puts it away.* It's safer in the suitcase anyway. I don't want to lose it. Well, I can't sit around here all night. *Trying to close suitcase.* I'd better go somewhere . . . Come on, you worked before. *Getting frustrated with suitcase clasp.* Stupid suitcase.

As she struggles with it, two ragged children have snuck up behind her and lean on the bench. Ellen is about ten; her brother is two years younger. Both wear warm but well-lived-in clothes. They are a bit scruffy but very cheerful.

Ellen: Whatcha got in the suitcase?

Amy: *Startled.* Who are you?

Ellen: Ellen Carter and this is my little brother, Bobby. *Bobby crosses his eyes sociably.* What you got in the suitcase?

Amy: All my worldly possessions.

Bobby: What's that?

Amy: *Opening case.* Well, my skates, my toothbrush.

Bobby: What's this here?

Amy: My harmonica. I got it for Christmas last year but I never learned to play it yet. And the nightgown my grandma gave me. And this is my favorite sweater. And my baseball glove. I wanted this glove so bad, it's just right for third base. I told my mom about it all the time and she'd just nod and say "Um-hm" like she wasn't listening, but when I opened up my birthday presents there it was, the exact same glove I wanted.

Bobby: *Pulling flowered long underwear from the suitcase and donning them like a toque or a jester's cap.* Underpants! Underpants!

Amy: *Snatching them back.* Those are for winter.

Ellen: Are you running away from home?

Amy: No. I'm just looking for a better environment to grow up in.

Bobby: A what?

Ellen: Why don't you live here?

Amy: Here?

Ellen: In the park. We do most of the time. Except when it's time to eat or sleep. My mom locks the door so we live here most of the time except when we go to school, or when there's something interesting somewheres else, like fixing the street or a car accident or something. We could get food from home for you and if you got a blanket you could sleep under a tree.

Amy: I think I'd be too scared to sleep all by myself out here.

Ellen: You wouldn't be all by yourself. There's always teenage guys with their girlfriends coming here, and the dogs come around at night, and the rubbies . . .

Amy: Grubbies?

Ellen: Rubbies. Old men that drink wine and vanilla and fall asleep in the park.

Amy: *To Bobby who is handling plastic packet.* That's my rainsuit. There's a rain jacket with a hood and rain pants in there.

Bobby: In here?

Amy: Yup, all folded up . . . *As Bobby takes it out.* Be careful you don't rip it. You mean they drink vanilla like you put in whipping cream?

Ellen: I guess so.

Amy: I tried drinking some once, when I was little. I thought if a little bit of it in something tasted good, then a whole bunch by itself must taste really good.

Ellen: Did it?

Amy: No.

Bobby: School books. You're running away from home and taking your school books?

Amy: Sure.

Bobby: What's this?

Amy: That's my telescope. *Pulling it open.* You look through this end.

Bobby: Just like a pirate. A space pirate. *In robot voice.* Space Pirate Captain Carter, here is your starscope which you left in the bathtub.

Ellen: Thank you, X-37.

Bobby: That's not how pirates talk. They talk like *Robert Newton.* AARRR, Fetch me my cheese, robot, and a bottle of rum.

Ellen: That's how old time pirates talk, Bobby.

Bobby: Space pirates too.

Ellen: This is our spaceship. Mostly it's just the bridge, but sometimes the whole ship. We play space a lot. We figure John Carter, Warlord of Mars, must have been an ancestor of ours.

Bobby: *Robot.* Now that we have the princess in our power, Captain, shall we swoop down upon that space vehicle and plunder it?

Amy: Am I the princess?

Ellen: I'm the captain, he's X-37, I guess you're the princess.

Bobby: *Robot.* The princess will tell the ship we are friendly and once they let their shields down we will plunder them.

Amy: I will not.

Bobby: *Robot.* Then we will feed you to the space dogs. *He and Ellen become space dogs, growl and gnash a moment.*

Amy: I'd rather die than betray my people.

Bobby: Communication from other ship, Captain.

Ellen: Ar, right, make the princess unconscious, X-37.

Bobby extends his arm and makes robot-hissing noises.

Bobby: That's gas that knocks you out. *Amy swoons.*

Ellen: *To viewing screen.* Hello, Ahoy. We've rescued your princess from pirates. We'll beam her aboard if you let up your

screens. Show them the princess, X-37. *Bobby hoists up Amy.*
You're letting your screens down now? Good, Over and out. Har,
har.

Amy: *Waking.* Where am I? Oh! *To Bobby at controls.* What are
you doing, robot?

Bobby: Preparing photon torpedoes.

Amy: What does that button do?

Bobby: That is the torpedo launcher.

Amy: And that?

Bobby: That is the self-destruct lever.

Ellen: X-37, you fool . . .

Amy pulls lever, all explode and fall to ground.

After a pause, all lying on ground. What grade are you in?

Amy: Six. What grade are you in?

Ellen: Four. I was supposed to be in five but I flunked last year.
Don't get in the house enough to do much homework. You won't
get much chance to do homework living in the park, either. It gets
too dark. Do you know why cats get stuck up in trees when they
climb?

Amy: No.

Ellen: Their claws go like this, see? *Holding hands up with
fingers crooked forwards.* So they won't hold them in if they climb
down frontwards, and they're scared to go down backwards 'cause
they can't see. I asked the park guy when a cat got stuck up a tree
once. So there's lots of stuff you can learn living here, but none of it
ever came up on any of my tests.

Amy: I don't think I'd feel safe living here anyway.

Ellen: Don't pick your scab, Bobby. He hurt his arm falling out of
a tree. It might have got infected but I washed it out with shampoo
. . . Why don't you go to a group home?

Amy: What's that?

Ellen: It's a home for kids that don't live with their parents.
There's one on Arlington Street.

Amy: Just the kids live there?

Ellen: No. They got workers that cook and look after them. Come
on, I'll show you.

Amy: I can't close my suitcase.

Bobby: Let me try.

Ellen: *To Bobby.* I told you not to pick at that. Maybe I should have used soap, but the shampoo seemed to make more bubbles. *To Amy.* I don't remember you from school. You go to Mulvey?

Amy: No, Laura Secord. Why don't you and Bobby come and live in the group home too?

Ellen: We already got a home.

Amy: But if your mom locks you out of the house all the time . . .

Ellen: She's got things to do. And she gets headaches. What's to do in the house anyway? Watch TV and do homework? SSSH! *Westminster church bells chime 8:00 p.m.* Come on, Bobby, time to go home.

Amy: Wait! I don't know where I'm going.

Ellen: That red house just down there. The one with the bicycle rack in the front yard. Just tell 'em you want to talk to who's on duty. If it's Janice, just tell her your mom hits you, she likes that. Come on, Bobby.

Amy: Wait . . .

They've gone. Amy walks to the group home. Barney, a sullen boy three years older than Amy, is lounging on the front steps, reading a comic.

Amy: Hello . . . My name's Amy . . . I've come to live here.

Barney: *Yelling over his shoulder.* Janice! *To Amy.* Nobody told me there was a new kid coming. Who sent you?

Amy: Ellen and Bobby.

Barney: Who? What agency are they with?

Amy: Agency?

Barney: You know. Children's Aid or Welfare or what?

Amy: I don't know. They didn't tell me.

Barney: Janice! *Christine, thirteen, heavily made-up, comes onto the porch.*

Chris: She's upstairs counselling Howard. Who's your friend, Barney?

Barney: What's your name?

Amy: Amy Hebinski.

Barney: Hebinski?

Chris: I'm Christine.

Barney: She says she's moving in. Did Children's Aid take you away from home or did you run away?

Amy: Neither, I just left.

Barney: Janice! Janice!

Janice: *Off.* What is it?

Barney: Come here. I want to talk to you.

Janice: I'm talking to Howard, you can wait your turn.

Barney: Come here now!

Janice: Stop yelling, I'll come down when I'm done.

Barney: Shut up yourself. Who made you the hot number around here all of a sudden?

Chris: Don't mind Barney. His uncle was supposed to come in from out of town today and never showed up. Why'd you leave your mother? Did she beat you up?

Amy: No, of course not.

Chris: It's nothing to be ashamed of. My mom used to beat me up all the time. Last time she broke my arm so they took me away and put me here. Yelling back and forth in court and everything. Your mom got lots of boyfriends?

Amy: I think that's my mom's business and not anyone else's.

Chris: Janice would never let you off with that. She says everybody in the house should know everything about everybody else in the house 'cause then we'll all trust each other. But don't trust Barney when you're playing Monopoly. He cheats.

Barney: I do not.

Chris: When you're the banker all those hundred dollar bills just crawl up your arm and hide themselves in your shirt pocket all on their own, eh?

Amy: I don't think I'd like anybody knowing everything about me. Not just anybody.

Chris: It's not just anybody, it's like part of your family here. That's what Janice says. Your mom knows everything about you, doesn't she?

Amy: Just about, I guess.

Chris: And that doesn't bother you, eh? So?

Amy: But that's different.

Chris: So, why don't you tell me a little about yourself?

Amy: Like what?

Chris: How old are you?

Amy: Eleven.

Chris: You got any brothers and sisters?

Amy: No. Do you work here?

Chris: Just till Janice comes down . . .

Barney: No, she doesn't work here. She just gets off on playing counsellor.

Chris: Barney's so immature.

Amy: Do you live here?

Chris: Yeah.

Amy: Is it a nice place to live?

Chris: I guess so. Where'd you get the suitcase?

Amy: It's my mom's.

Chris: Did you steal it?

Amy: No—I just borrowed it.

Chris: Did your father get married to somebody else?

Amy: No. He lives with a lady and her kids.

Chris: Don't you get jealous of your father living with other kids?

Amy: No. Why should I?

Chris: I don't think you're telling the truth.

Amy: Why should I get jealous of Marcy and Blaine, they're such spoiled brats. The only reason my dad lives with them is because Helen is their mother.

Janice: *Coming onto porch.* Okay Barney, what was so important? *Janice is in her late twenties. She's been a child care worker about three years. She still tries, but very wearily.*

Chris: We've got a new girl come to live here.

Janice: Nobody told me about that.

Barney: Nobody told me neither.

Janice: Who brought you here?

Amy: Nobody.

Janice: Somebody had to. You can't just move in here. Who's your worker?

Amy: My what?

Janice: The person who looks after your case.

Amy: Oh, it's my mom's case. I just borrowed it.

Janice: Are you a ward of the court? You can't live here unless you're a ward of the court.

Amy: What's that?

Janice: Oh dear. Maybe you should tell me a little about yourself. What's your name?

Amy: Amy Hebinski.

Janice: I don't think I have a file on a Hebinski. Somebody should have sent me your file.

Chris: She's a runaway.

Janice: Is that true, Amy?

Chris: She ran away from her mother. She's eleven years old. Her father lives with another woman.

Janice: Did your mother mistreat you? Does she hit you?

Amy: No, I mean yes.

Janice: She does?

Amy: Ellen said I should tell you she does.

Janice: Who's Ellen?

Amy: I don't know her last name. I met her in the park.

Janice: You'd better give me your mother's phone number and address. I'll have to contact Children's Aid and your mother. Then if your mother has been mistreating you, we'll have to take the case to court. You might be placed in a home, perhaps this one.

Amy: But my mom never mistreated me, hardly; I only said that 'cause Ellen told me to, and I'm already away from home so why go to court?

Janice: It's the law. Now, what's your phone number and address?

Amy: I don't want to go to court.

Barney: *Off.* Janice! The stove's on fire again!

Janice: *To Amy.* You stay put. *Running off.* How many times do I have to tell you not to use that back burner? Where's the baking soda?

As soon as Janice is gone, Amy begins dragging away her suitcase.

Chris: Hey, where do you think you're going? *Amy's gone.* Hey Janice. The kid that ran away, ran away! *Exits.*

Amy wanders back into the park and sits on the bench. She starts and looks over her shoulder. Dejectedly, She opens the suitcase, takes out her harmonica and tentatively blows a few notes.

Amy: It sure makes a lonely sound. Even when you don't know how to play it.

Blows a little more. Stops. In the distance a harmonica sound playing "The Crawdad Song". It comes closer. A grizzle-bearded

*man in tattered clothing, carrying a plastic shopping bag, playing
a harmonica in a rack, mumbling to himself, singing snatches of
the song and digging through the bottles in the garbage cans.*

Ben: You get a line and I'll get a pole, honey . . . *Going through
bottles in trash.* Wine, wine—good for nothing—damn kids beat
me to the beer bottles again—buying candy with my groceries.
You get a line, I'll get a pole, babe . . . What're you staring at?

Amy: Nothing.

Ben: What'd you call me?

Amy: Nothing—I mean . . .

Ben: You better mean, miss. Think you're looking at some any
old soused out old vagabond? Damn your eyes. Where'd you get
the suitcase?

Amy: I borrowed it. It's my mom's.

Ben: Trade you my bag for it. Big old case for a little mite like you
to carry around.

Amy: It's on wheels.

Ben: Think I'm blind? See a lot of things you don't. Seen the
ghosts of dawn. Call me a liar, it's true. You get a line, I'll get a
pole, we'll both go down to the crawdad hole. *Finishes on the
harmonica. Finding rusted sprocket in trash.* Things those damn
fools throw away. *Sitting down to dab at rust with rag from
pocket.* Cogs and gears, miss, that's all there is. Sprockets and
chains. Whole damn world's just one huge watch works, all
interlocked, ticking away. You look like you just sprung yourself
out of the works. You running away from home?

Amy: No. I'm just looking for another place to live.

Ben: Old man giving you a rough time? Gave me a rough time.
Tool Steel. Clean 'er up, polish 'er, and she'll shine. Not like
chrome or no nickle-plate, but she'll shine. Mount her on good
bearings she'll spin in the wind. Got a hundred of 'em stuck on the
outside of the shack. Wind comes up, they spin and shine, all on
their own. *Spinning sprocket on a pencil from his pocket.* Not one
of them linked to another, not two of 'em touching, just turning
alone in the wind. You sit and watch that on a sunny afternoon, or
in the sunset when they all glow red and gold, it'll ease open
whatever's wound up inside you. *He has stuffed the sprocket into
his bag and is continuing his search through the trash.* Old man
giving you a rough time?

Amy: My father doesn't live with us, just me and my mom.

Ben: *Who has found old basketball sneaker.* You know, if you could cut this apart and make the pieces into two sneakers they'd be about the size of the pair I bought my kid. Wife told me they were laughing at him in school 'cause he wore rags so I start with what I could. *Holding out sneaker as half a pair.* Look what I brung you, son. Wife said they're cheap junk; if you can't do better than the bargain bins at Kresge's I'll find someone who can. Wake up in the morning and they're gone. Took the damn sneakers with them, though, good enough for running off in. What happened to For better or worse, eh? For richer or for poorer? I tried! *Suddenly notices sneaker in new light, sits down and tries its sole against one of his worn-out shoes.* There's only one lesson worth learning, miss. Don't ever want nothing from nobody. Be satisfied inside your own skin. *Proceeds to remove shoe and don sneaker.*

Amy: But everybody needs friends, and a family.

Ben: What for?

Amy: You know. To care about, and to care about you, and to help each other, and to know each other.

Ben: So why'd you run off on your ma?

Amy: I need a normal family.

Ben: What's normal?

Amy: You know. Everyone knows that.

Ben: Maybe I do, but I don't think you do. Normal's average. Look. *From his bag he produces a dowel with four shiny gears suspended from it with string.* Now this here gear's two inches in diameter. This one's four inches, and this one's six inches, and this one's eight inches. Now what's the average of all them sizes?

Amy: What's the sizes again?

Ben: Eight inches, two, four and six.

Amy: That's twenty, divided by four is five.

Ben: Five inches. That's the average size of these gears. That's normal. But where's the five-inch gear? Where's that normal gear? There ain't none. It's just a number you got in your head; it don't mean nothing. Now don't you think it'd be awful silly for all these perfectly good little sprockets to start squeaking and complaining 'cause they weren't five inches in diameter so they aren't normal? Don't you?

Amy: I guess so.

Ben: So don't bother looking for no normal family.

Amy: But I can't live by myself.

Ben: Tell you what, I'll look after your suitcase for a few days while you're looking for work.

Amy: But I'm too young to work.

Ben: Ain't we all, ain't we all. But nobody's gonna support you.

Amy: My mom does.

Ben: Your mother loves you, miss. Nobody else does.

Amy: My dad does!

Ben: Guess you're right, miss. But he ain't around, is he? Gimme your suitcase.

Amy: No, Why should I?

Ben: *Looming over her.* 'Cause maybe I'll take it anyway and you won't get the joy of giving.

Amy: You wouldn't take my suitcase.

Ben: Maybe I would. Maybe I won't. *Moving off.* Take care of yourself, miss. Ain't nobody else going to. Find yourself an old shack somewhere, you won't need nobody. *He's gone.*

Amy: But everybody needs somebody, everybody needs a family— I don't even know what a family is any more.

The lights come up on the interior of a corner grocery store. Mrs. Vogel, in her early sixties, is yattering at Gregor, the middle-aged storekeeper, who is adding up her groceries behind the counter.

Mrs. Vogel: As I was saying, the children these days, always getting into trouble, out at all hours of the night, it's the fault of their parents. Or parent, I should say. So many of them being brought up without fathers. If a woman can't keep a marriage together, she shouldn't be allowed to have children.

Amy comes in and walks dejectedly to the dairy case. Mrs. Vogel, without breaking vocal stride, glances at Amy then at her watch.

Mrs. Vogel: They claim they love their children, but if they really loved them they wouldn't try bringing them up alone like that. The government should take the poor little dears away from them and put them in good homes. *Gregor counts her change out silently.* There's plenty of young couples who would be happy to take them. *She picks up her bagged groceries.*

Gregor: *Fairly thick East-European accent.* Well, always nice having conversation with you, Mrs. Vogel. *As Mrs. Vogel exits, Amy drifts towards the counter, carrying a half pint of chocolate milk.*

Mrs. Vogel: And what are you doing out at this time of night? You see what I mean? *She is gone.*

Gregor: Come along, den. Time I closed up the store.

Amy: But I thought I could drink it in here.

Gregor: *Ringing up milk on till.* No, is past closing already. Chocolate milk is tventy-saven sants.

Amy: But it's cold out there. I just want to get warm. I've been walking around all night. *Becoming tearful.* I tried everywhere I could think of. But the Pirellis were too noisy, and Kevin Gremlin is too weird, and George and Irma, and everything. And I just need to get warm so I can think of somewhere to go.

Gregor: Don't you have a home to go to, little person?

Amy: No. I did have, sort of.

Gregor: You had home yes, I understant; you had home no, I understant; you had home sort of I don't make no sense of.

Amy: Well, to have a real home you have to have a family, and there was just my mom and me and that's not really a family.

Gregor: What's missing dat it's not a {amily?

Amy: Two people can't be a family.

Gregor: I navver knew dat rule. I always tought anytime pipple make a home togadder and try halp ich udder gat along, you got family. Sometimes you don't iven need a home, though is badder whan you got one. Here, sit down, rest you self a bit. I close up . . . *Proceeds to do so.* You and your mama, you don't get along?

Amy: We get along all right most of the time; except when she's writing exams.

Gregor: She goes to school, too? Must give you a lot to talk about.

Amy: Sometimes.

Gregor: Listen, little person, I tall you something. Maybe sometimes your mama does things you don't like or make you angry. My wife, Vilmena, she grinds her teeth whan she sleeps. Tvanty years, like slipping next to Russian army marching through snow. Crunch, crunch, crunch. Some nights whan I can't slip, worrying about store, worrying about bills, and shi's lying dere, Crunch, Crunch. I say to myself, Gregor, you gat up, gat dressed, put couple pairs wool socks and couple sandwiches in your pocket, go out the door and navver have to listen again to Crunch, Crunch. But I navver did. Is my family, how can I live dem? If you go away from pipple dat aren't exactly in avry ditail what you want them in your mind to be, you gonna grow up to be a varry lonely old woman.

Amy: Can I stay here?

Gregor: Here? No—wall, maybe you got idea dere.

Mrs. Gregor: *Off.* Gregor! Aren't you closed up yet? I've warmed up dinner for you.

Gregor: I be up soon. Chust couple things to take care of first. *To Amy.* Stay here? I could use little halp around store. You grown up now. Don't need your mother no more, you need job. You a strong girl?

Amy: I am. I play baseball and hockey and . . .

Gregor: You used to play hockey. Working girl now, got no time for hockey. Lift that box of cans.

Amy: This one?

Gregor: Dat one. No! Not like dat, you break your back lifting havvy tings like dat. Tink you're big crane like construction work? Band down like dis, den your legs do the work. Good. Now see if you can carry over to dere . . . Now dis ting is for punching on prices, like dis. Chust punch price on top and put cans on shelf with udders. *Amy begins to do so.* Maybe you can work hard enough you can stay here.

Amy: And live with your family?

Gregor: No, no. You live in shed out back. Clean it up a little bit, you won't be dere much except for slipping, anyway. Lots to do. Wash floors every day, wax once a week, shelves to stock, windows to wash, delivery trucks to unload. You gat up maybe six o'clock—NO! four o'clock in morning, work copple hours before school, copple hours after school, all day on weekends, maybe is worth my while to kip you on.

Amy: But I have to get time off to do my homework.

Gregor: Well, maybe you have enough time for schoolwork. But you being working girl now, maybe you should think of dropping out of school.

Amy: I have to be able to go home sometimes.

Gregor: Sure, every night you go home out back to the shack.

Amy: Shack! I mean my home, where my mom is. I have to be able to visit my mom . . .

Gregor: You think she want you to visit her? Maybe since you run away from her she feels so hurt she won't want to see you avver again.

Amy: Sometimes before I did things that hurt her and she still wanted me to be there.

Gregor: Did you avver live her before?

Amy: No.

Gregor: So. Somebody get their heart broken, eventually heals up in time if left alone. But they see the person that broke it, start to hurt all over again. You want to hurt your mama? *Waxing melodramatic.* If one of my kids run away like that I never vant to see that kid again. You want to see your mama, maybe you sneak back one night and watch her through window. *Holding up hands, thumbs extended, like a window frame.* There she is. Look. But she don't see you, so she don't get hurt. *The two of them look through the window.*

Amy: Mom?

Gregor walks back to counter, surreptitiously glancing back at Amy. Amy suddenly gets up and runs out door.

Gregor: Where you going?

Amy: I'm going home! *She's gone.*

Gregor: For little person with big suitcase she sure run fast. Gregor, you should have been actor. *Picks up milk and drinks it.*

Mrs. Gregor: Oh boy, Gregor!

Gregor: Coming, coming. Velmina, guess what—big surprise. Remember that fellow Gregor went to work this morning? Who's coming home? Is Marlon Brando! *Exits.*

Amy's mother's apartment, Teresa comes in the door; followed by Fred. Teresa's about thirty, dressed in a contemporary style. Fred is the same age. He is uncertain how to relate to Amy and to Teresa when Amy is around.

Teresa: Amy! She must be asleep. Sit down, would you like a cup of coffee?

Fred: Sure.

Teresa: *Starting off.* I'll just look in on her.

Fred: Your place is always so neat compared to mine.

Teresa: I have a conscientious daughter. *She is off in the bedroom.*

Fred: Sounds like a useful article. Know where I could pick one up?

Teresa: *Off.* No.

Fred idly looks through the papers on the table.

Teresa: *Coming back on.* I'm trying not to panic, but my daughter isn't there.

Fred: You sure?

Teresa: There's only so many places you can put an eleven-year-old girl in this apartment. *Dialing phone.* Maybe she's downstairs with Mrs. Bates watching TV. She must have been down there when I called before. Hello, Mrs. Bates, it's Terry O'Connel from upstairs. Is Amy with you? *Fred finds note and glances at it.* Have you seen her tonight? No, it's all right, thank you. *Hangs up.*

Fred: Maybe you should take a look at this . . . it looks pretty official.

Teresa: "Ms. Teresa O'Connel . . . Wolseley Street . . . Dear Mother, this is your daughter Amy writing. I won't be there when you get home. I don't think we can live together any more." *Skims letter silently for a moment.* Oh dear. She says she hates it when you call her Snooks and pinch her cheek. Says if she was a dog she'd bite your thumbs off. "I think you've given a good try at raising a daughter by yourself, but I think I need more of a family. Goodbye." She really is gone.

Fred: Where could she go? Does she have any relatives in the city?

Teresa: I'd better call her father. *As Teresa dials there's a timid knock at the door which only the audience hears.* Hello Frank? It's Teresa. Have you heard anything from Amy tonight? She's gone. I don't know where. *The door opens a crack and Amy sticks her head through.* How long will it take you to get here? All right. We'll wait for you. *She hangs up the phone, Amy is inside the door now.*

Fred: Uh, Teresa . . . *He points to Amy.*

Teresa: *She turns, sees Amy and crosses to her quickly.* Where have you been? *Hugs her.*

Amy: Is it all right if I come home now?

Teresa: You are home.

Amy: The man at the grocery store said you might not want me to come back.

Teresa: Of course I want you back. What a stupid thing for him to say. Come inside, I have to phone your father back and tell him you're home. Fred, bar the door or something.

She goes to the phone, Amy comes in and sits at the table. Fred closes the door and crosses to the table, staring at his hands with the thumbs folded in.

Amy: What are you doing?

Fred: Trying to imagine what I'd look like without thumbs. I guess Snooks is a pretty stupid name to call somebody.

Amy: It sure is.

Teresa: *Coming from phone.* I caught him as he was going out the door. You must be starving.

Amy: I ate dinner at the Pirellis. A rubbie wanted to steal your suitcase in the park, but I wouldn't let him.

Teresa: A rubbie? I told you I didn't want you going in the park after dark. Anything could've happened . . .

Amy: He didn't hurt me.

Fred: Well, I'd better get going, leave you two to your homecoming.

Teresa: *Kissing his cheek.* I'll call you tomorrow.

Fred: Okay. So long, Snooks. *Realizes what he said.* I'm going to have to think of another name to call you. Maybe Gazooli or Mundigoomer . . .

Amy: How about Amy?

Fred: Not bad, not bad. "Amy"—not bad. I'll give it a try. Bye. *Exits.*

Amy: Is it okay if I don't unpack 'till tomorrow? I'm tired.

Teresa: As long as you don't wake up in the morning and decide since the suitcase is still packed you might as well run away again.

Amy: I'm never going to do that again.

Teresa: Good. I'm glad you came back.

Amy: So am I . . . An old woman in the store said the government should take me away from you and give me to somebody else.

Teresa: I'd like to see them try.

■

The Other Side of the Pole

Marney Heatley, Stephen Heatley, and Edward Connell

*Marianne Copithorne, **Mylar**, and Robert Winslow, **Willy**, in the 1983
Theatre Network production.*

photograph: Russ Hewitt

The Other Side of the Pole was commissioned by Theatre Network
and was first performed at the Red Deer College Theatre, Red Deer
Alberta on November 10,1982 in a co-production between Theatre
Network and Centre Stage. The current version was first per-
formed by Theatre Network at E.W. Pratt School in High Prairie,
Alberta on December 4, 1983 with the following cast:

Willy _____ Robert Winslow
Lectro (John Smith) _____ Raymond Storey
Baubles (Alex Kringle) _____ Bradley C. Rudy
Sparkle (Sandy Kringle) _____ Lydia Slabyj
Marzipan (Pix Kringle) _____ Jan Henderson
Mylar _____ Marianne Copithorne

Directed by Stephen Heatley
Designed by Daniel Van Heyst

Musical direction: Edward Connell
Stage management: Linda Graham
Technical direction: Mel Geary
Production: Jane Buss

Information regarding the music and performance rights should
be directed to:

Theatre Network
11845 - 77 Street
Edmonton, Alberta
Canada   T5B 2G3

Prologue

The scene takes place in the shipping room at Santa's workshop at the North Pole. The room is filled with boxes that are about to be shipped all over the world. There is also a piano and a calendar which reads December 14. Willy enters sanding a block and looking for Baubles.

Willy: Baubles! *Pause. No response.* Baubles! Baubles, are you back from the sleigh-port yet?

There is no response. Willy realizes that the calendar has not been changed. He rips off December 14, counts the number of days until Christmas and begins sanding in earnest. Sparkle enters. She is checking the crates for shipment and discovers that they are all labelled incorrectly.

Willy: Oh, hi Sparkle.

Sparkle: Hi Willy. Is Baubles back with the new elf yet?

Willy: No. Guess what Sparkle? It's only ten days until Christmas.

Sparkle screams and runs out almost knocking over Lectro who is trying to get a small computer to function properly.

Lectro: Is Baubles back with that new elf!?

Willy: No.

Lectro: Well, what's he waiting for? Christmas?

They both start to laugh, then . . .

Lectro: That's not funny.

Marzipan: *Enters on the run.* I've lost my eyes! Has anybody seen my eyes? *Discovers her package of doll eyes in her pocket.* Ooooo. What's keeping Baubles?

Baubles: *From off.* We're here! We're here!

All the elves gather to welcome Baubles and their new helper.

Mylar: Ah, Baubles—you don't mind if I call you Bob—who's the cute little number with the red nose?

Baubles: That's Rudolph.

Mylar: Rudolph. Right. Hey and I love that striped pole with the North Pole sign on it.

Baubles: This *is* the North Pole.

Mylar: Too much. This place cracks me up.

Baubles: Now don't lollygoggle. I've got dozens of Christmas ornaments for you to decorate.

They arrive in the area where all the other elves are waiting. Baubles realizes he is going to have to introduce her to them.

Baubles: Ah, this is the new elf, Mylar.

Mylar: How're you doing?

They all charge her and try to carry her off in all directions except for Willy.

Willy: Hey! That's not very nice. We should tell her who we are and welcome her to Santa's workshop.

They all agree and let her go.

Baubles: That's Willy. He's in charge while Santa and Crumhorn are away picking up orders.

Willy: That's me. I do blocks.

Sparkle: Sparkle. Wrapping.

Mylar: Too much.

Marzipan: Marzipan. Dolls.

Mylar: Fabulous.

Lectro: I'm Lectro. I do electronics.

Mylar: Great!

Lectro: *Grabbing her.* I think so too!

They all grab for her and lift her off the ground.

Mylar: Hold on! Put me down. Gently. *They do.* Okay. It's nice to be here and everything but I can't work everywhere at once.

Marzipan: Well, I need you first!

The others protest and start toward Mylar again.

Mylar: Whoa! Look, what is the big rush? Isn't it about time for a coffee break?

Baubles: Coffee break? That's a good one. I have another twenty dozen ornaments to paint.

Lectro: And everyone wants a new video toy this year.

Marzipan: None of my dolls have eyes yet.

Sparkle: And everything has to be custom wrapped!

Baubles: We'll have to work day and night to make the deadline.

Mylar: Deadline? What deadline?

All: Christmas!

Willy: December 24th is Christmas Eve.

Mylar: Hey, cool it with the deadlines. Let's have coffee. People will wait.

All: Not for Christmas!

Mylar: Hey, I don't know much about this Christmas business but I do know what one of your problems is. If this is the way that you work all the time, then . . .

Efficiency is your Deficiency

Mylar:
Efficiency is your deficiency
Productivity is my proclivity.
So you gotta know that to make it go
You gotta move, gotta groove, gotta make it prove
That you got what it takes to make the breaks,
To call the shots to connect the dots.
Make it fly to the sky; make it run to the sun;
Make it hop to the top; make it never stop;
Make it go go go go go go go
Get down! Uh huh!

Marzipan: Get down?

Lectro: Uh huh.

Mylar:
Now I'll articulate how you facilitate
To make this place circumnavigate.
But you gotta know that to make it go
You gotta fly, gotta try, gotta get it by.
So here's the route, the way to shoot,
The way to aim, to win the game.
Make it walk, make it talk
Make it blink, make it wink
Make it bump, make it jump
Don't let it slump
Make it go go go go go go go
Get down! Uh huh!

Baubles: Get down?

Sparkle: Uh huh!

The elves seem to be caught up in the rhythm of this odd song. Willy watches in horror as they begin to twitch and jerk and, eventually dance.

Mylar:
Now the minimum is your optimum
'Cause the medium is to overcome
So you gotta know where you gotta go
You gotta plan if you can, make it spic and span
So keep it clean, make the scene
Wash it down, go to town
Make it fast, make it last
Make it fine, make it shine
Make it bright, make it right
Make it out of sight
Make it go go go go go go go
Get down! Uh huh!

All (except Willy): Get down! Uh huh!

Mylar:
So mobilize to reorganize
And you'll realize, how to actualize
What ya gotta know, where ya gotta go
How to spin how to win
How to bring it in
So you pull the stock
You tend the flock
You shake it loose
You cook the goose
You pull the lead
You paint it red
You climb the walls
You deck the halls!
So up, down, turn it round!
Up, down, turn it round!
I say up, down, turn it round.
Make it snap, use a map
Make it art, use a chart
Make efficiency your directory

All (except Willy): Make it go go go go go go go go go go go go go
Get down!
Wah!

*There is a big flourish finish and then they all realize how carried
away they were. The elves are a bit ashamed of their behaviour.*

Lectro: Get down.

All: Uh huh.

Sparkle: I don't think she understands what Christmas is all about, Willy.

Willy: Yeah. *To Mylar.* You see, here at the North Pole, we put a little love into everything we make.

Mylar: *Rolling her eyes.* Oh.

Lectro: Yes. That's true. Funny, you know—she sounds like somebody from the A. B. C.

They all gasp and run for cover.

Mylar: What's that?

Lectro: The Assignation for the Brandishment of Christmas!

Baubles: No, the Association for the Banishment of Christmas.

They all react again to the lethal words.

Marzipan: Are you a spy?

Mylar: I've never heard of the A. B. C. And I am definitely not a spy. *They all relax.* Say, I think maybe I'm not the person for this job, whatever it is. I think I'd be best to catch the next sleigh out of here.

All: No, you can't go.

Baubles: We need you or we'll never be ready in time.

Mylar: But I don't think I can work the way you do. It doesn't make any sense to me.

Baubles: We're not usually this disorganized.

Willy: No. But Christmas is on the upswing.

Marzipan: We were just caught short-handed.

Sparkle: And people are counting on us.

Baubles: Last year at this time we had a surplus of stock. Look— *Shows his records.* 453,000 rag dolls, 25,000 hula hoops . . .

Lectro: And don't forget all the singing giraffes on the music boxes—"I'm Dreaming of a White Christmas."

Mylar: *Interrupting.* Hey, I don't dig it. I've heard about this Christmas stuff somewhere, but that was a long time ago. Nobody actually believes in it, do they?

Willy: Oh yeah, they do.

Marzipan: More than ever.

Mylar: But why?

They all try to explain it to her at once.

Willy: Well, remember what happened in Split Hoof?

All: Right. Split Hoof. That's where it started. That's it.

Baubles: Just last year.

Lectro: Tell the story, Willy. I've heard it a hundred times but I still love it.

Marzipan: It'll make everything clear.

Baubles: Tell her about the barber shop and the magic pole that glowed.

Lectro: And about the letter and the mailbox!

Sparkle: And how they cut out the decorations and decorated the shop.

Marzipan: And how they ripped all the pages about Christmas out of the library books!

Willy: Okay, okay. How should I start?

All: Once upon a time.

Willy: Right. Once upon a time, there was Split Hoof and a barber shop and there was no Christmas and . . .

They all interrupt to remind him of their favourite part.

Willy: I don't know how to say it!

Baubles: *Simply.* Okay, we'll all tell it. *Agreed.*

Willy: Okay, Sparkle, you play my friend Sandy, 'cause you're the youngest.

Marzipan: I'm artistic, so I'll be Pix.

Baubles: Do I have to be the dad?

Lectro: Yes. You're the biggest.

Baubles: Oh . . . that means I'm the . . . *They all shush him.*

Lectro: Who will we get to play Willy?

They all form a huddle except for Willy. They break from the huddle? Look at Willy and then . . .

All: Nah.

Willy: Hey, I *am* Willy. That's me!

All: Okay.

Baubles: *To Lectro.* That means you'll have to play . . .

All: John Smith! *Great laughter.*

Sparkle: *To Mylar.* So, what do you think?

Mylar: Well, the next sleigh out of here isn't until tonight, so . . . alright.

Willy: Hey, if we're going to have a barber shop, we need a barber pole.

Lectro: I know what we could use.

There is another huddle.

Marzipan: That old striped thing?

Lectro: Santa won't mind as long as we put it back.

Baubles: I'll write it down so we don't forget.

Willy and Lectro usher Mylar into her seat as Baubles writes it down. At this point the stage is set for the beginning of the story. The "overture" happens while this action is going on.

Overture—The Other Side of the Pole

The overture is a collage of well-known Christmas songs that are underscored by a magical sounding musical accompaniment.

Baubles: Joy to the world the Lord is come, let earth receive her . . .

Women: Sleep in heavenly peace, sleep in heavenly . . .

Lectro: Joyful all ye nations rise, Join the triumph of the skies . . .

Women/Baubles: Dashing through the snow, in a one-horse open sleigh . . .

Women: Gloria in excelsis deo . . .

Baubles: On the fifth day of Christmas my true love gave to me . . .

Men: Five gold rings!

Women: Oh come let us adore him, Oh come let us adore him . . .

Women/Baubles: Then how the reindeer loved him, As they shouted out with glee . . .

Lectro: Fa la la la la la la la la . . .

All: We wish you a merry Christmas, we wish you a merry Christmas, we wish you a merry Christmas, and a happy New Year . . .

Baubles/Sparkle/Marzipan:
When you travel through a dream,
Things are never what they seem.
Everything's a big surprise,
You simply won't believe your eyes.

Willy and Lectro arrive with the pole. They join in the singing.

Nothing does what it should do.
Nothing's false and nothing's true.

There are things you can't control
When you're on the other side of the pole.

The pole is placed in a prominent place and on the last note of the music, it lights up. Willy and Lectro take their places with Mylar to watch the story as Marzipan, Sparkle and Baubles prepare for Scene One.

Act 1
Scene 1

The lights come up on the barber shop. There is a barber chair and a table with barber paraphernalia on it and chairs for waiting customers. There is a striped barber pole visible outside the shop. Pix is sitting in the barber chair putting the finishing touches on a toy she is making. Sandy is sitting in one of the other chairs reading a mystery novel and chewing gum. Suddenly the door bursts open and Alex storms in. He paces for a few seconds. Pix and Sandy give each other knowing glances.

Alex: That woman is going to drive me mad!

Pix: What woman, dear?

Alex: Elvira Witherspoon, who else? She spent the whole morning in my office whining and crying. I tell you, it's tough enough being mayor in this town without that woman badgering me day and night about one thing or another. Last week she was complaining that there was smut in Grade One readers. I'd be surprised if she could even read one.

Pix: Relax Alex, you've just got to learn to ignore her.

Alex: Ignore her! That would be like trying to ignore a Sherman tank.

Pix: Well, you shouldn't let her get you so upset.

Alex: *Shouting.* I am not upset!

Pix: Yes you are, dear.

Alex: *Calming himself.* I am not upset, I'm just sick and tired of that trouble-making old bat telling me how to do my job.

Pix: You're the mayor: you're supposed to do what people want.

Alex: Elvira Witherspoon is not a good representative of the people of Split Hoof.

Pix: They voted her onto the town council.

Alex: Fifteen years ago. She may have been a good citizen then, but a lot of things have changed. She hasn't been the same since Major Witherspoon died.

Pix: Losing her husband was obviously hard on Elvira.

Alex: *Sarcastically.* It's been hard on me too.

Pix: You should try to be a little more sympathetic.

Alex: I'd be glad to if she didn't keep complicating things by trying to pass by-laws that would make life miserable for everyone. I always say, 'Simple is best.'

Pix: Her ideas are usually harmless enough.

Alex: Her latest campaign was to forbid people from chewing gum in public.

Sandy blows a bubble with her gum. It pops. Alex looks at her.

Pix: The dentists would like that.

Alex: And the gum chewers would lynch me!

Pix: Oh Alex, you're over-reacting. Thinking up laws makes Elvira feel important. She's just lonely.

Alex: Well, she's not alone anymore.

Pix: What do you mean?

Alex: Willy is back.

Music begins. The song is a mixture of sung lines and underscored dialogue.

Pix: I'd forgotten about Willy.

Sandy: *Sings.* Willy?

Alex: So had I.

Andy: *Sings.* Who is Willy?

Pix: *Spoken.* Mrs. Witherspoon's son.

Sandy: I didn't know Mrs. Witherspoon had a son.

Alex: Most people don't know, and Mrs. Witherspoon would like it to stay that way.

Sandy: Why? Is he a crook or something?

Pix: No, nothing like that.

Alex: Don't you have homework to do?

Sandy: I did it already.

Alex: Well, why don't you go outside and play?

Sandy: It's too cold. Besides—*Sings.* I want to hear about Willy.

Alex: *Spoken.* Willy is none of your business.

Pix: Is that why Elvira was in your office crying?

Alex: The institution he was in closed down. She's not too pleased at having him home again.

Sandy: Why? Doesn't she like him?

Pix: It's not that she doesn't like him, dear. It's just that Willy has a problem.

Sandy: Is he a loonie?

Alex: A loonie? Where do you pick up these ideas? *Sings.* Willy is . . . *Spoken.* Simple.

Sandy: What does that mean?

Pix: It means that he's not very smart. That's why he's been . . . 'away'.

Sandy: You mean his mother sent him away just because he didn't get good marks.

Alex: What?

Pix: *Sings.*
Willy is a grown man,
But he can't do things we can
For his mind
Is . . . behind
Willy is like a little boy

Sandy: *Spoken.* Boy, that sounds neat!

Alex: It's not neat. It's a disability.

Sandy: *Sings.* I hope Willy can stay here.

Alex: *Spoken.* There's no way that Willy can stay here. Mrs. Witherspoon asked me to find a new institution for Willy and I intend to do just that.

Sandy: Daddy . . .

Alex: Willy will be better off in an institution where there are trained people to look after him.

Sandy: Why can't his mother look after him?

Alex: I thought I told you to go outside and play.

Sandy: I think Mrs. Witherspoon is mean.

Alex: Don't you talk that way about one of our town's leading citizens.

Sandy: You said she was a trouble-making old bat.

Alex: I did not.

Pix: Yes, you did, dear.

Alex: Well, what if I did? She may be an unpleasant woman but you shouldn't say nasty things about your elders.

Sandy: That isn't fair.

Pix: *Sings.* Now Sandy . . .

Sandy: *Spoken.* Daddy can say mean things about her but I can't. What's fair about that?

Alex: *Sings threateningly.* Now Sandy . . .

Sandy: *Sings.*
I think Willy should stay
Tell my why
Should Willy have to go away.

Pix: *Spoken.* Willy will be happier in an institution.

Sandy: They'll put him in a loonie bin.

Pix: They won't put him in a loonie bin. They'll put him in a nice home where he can get all the care he needs.

Sandy: He already has a home. In Split Hoof.

Alex: What do you care about Willy anyway. You don't even know him.

Sandy: *Sings.* Willy sounds like lots of fun.

Alex: *Sings.*
He'd be hard on everyone.
He'd be a pest.

Sandy: *Spoken.* You said he was simple.

Alex: Well . . . ?

Sandy: You always say, *Sings.* 'Simple is best.'

Alex: *Spoken.* I do not.

Pix: Yes you do, dear.

Sandy: *Sings.* Willy sounds like a very special boy.

Pix: Sandy, you don't know anything about this Willy. You might not even like him.

Alex: She's not going to get a chance to find out either. I'm going to start calling institutions right away. *Heads for the phone. Sandy follows him.*

Sandy: Daddy, please don't.

Alex: Look. The longer Willy stays in town, the more unbearable Mrs. Witherspoon is going to get and the more unbearable she gets, the more bad tempered I'm going to get and the more bad tempered I get the more inclined I'll be to cut off your allowance.

Sandy: I don't care about that.

Pix: Don't get your father upset.

Alex: *To Pix.* It's too late. I'm already upset. *To Sandy.* You talk back to me once more and I'll warm your bottom.

Pix: Alex . . .

Sandy: I think both you and Mrs. Witherspoon are mean. Poor Willy likely never had anyone to love him. That's probably why he isn't very smart.

Pix: I don't think you understand Willy's problem.

Sandy: I don't think you have any feelings at all. *Picks up her coat and heads for the door.*

Alex: Where do you think you're going?

Sandy: Out to play!

She leaves, slamming the door behind her. The lights go down on the barber shop. The song ends. Willy and Lectro leave their seats to prepare for the next scene.

Interlude

Mylar: Well, that was all very nice but I think I'm going to wait at the sleigh port.

Willy: It's my part now!

Lectro: You cannot leave until the mail-box part!

Mylar: Alright, alright. I'll stay until the mailbox part!

Lectro leaves the stage. Willy prepares for his scene.

Scene 2

Sandy enters onto the street. She paces for a few seconds, fuming. She calms herself down and looks around her. She decides she will conjure up this 'Willy'. She closes her eyes and crosses her fingers, then calls softly.

Sandy: Willy. *Pause.* Willy. *Pause, then quickly.* Willy, Willy, Willy, Willy.

Willy enters behind Sandy. She opens her eyes and looks down the street in the opposite direction. She realises what a silly idea conjuring was and then turns and sees him. They startle each other. She composes herself.

Sandy: Are you Willy?

Willy nods.

Sandy: Mrs. Witherspoon's son?

Willy nods.

Sandy: Can you talk?

Willy nods.

Sandy: Well, talk then.

Willy: What should I say?

Sandy: You could start with 'Hello'.

Willy: Hello.

Sandy: *Sticking out her hand for him to shake.* Hi, my name's Sandy. I live over top of the barbershop with my dad and Pix.

Willy: Pix?

Sandy: Yeah, she's my mother but for some reason she likes me to call her Pix.

Willy: *Letting go of her hand.* I live over there now *He points.* with my mother, but I used to live somewhere else.

Sandy: In an institution. I know, 'cause my dad told me. Did you like living in an institution?

Willy: It was okay. I liked it.

Sandy: What did you do there?

Willy: Lots of things.

Sandy: Like what?

Willy: We learned things and sometimes we'd have parties and on Tuesdays we'd go swimming. I like swimming.

Sandy: It's too cold for swimming now.

Willy: The swimming pool I went to was inside a building. We went swimming even in the winter.

Sandy: Wow, that's neat. What else did you do?

Willy: We made things. Sometimes out of wood. I like building things out of wood. I sand them down real smooth so you can't ever get a sliver from them. See.

Willy takes a piece of wood from his pocket and hands it to Sandy. She feels it then hands it back to him.

Sandy: It feels nice. I wish we got to do stuff like that at my school. All we ever do is reading and arithmetic. You know, school stuff.

Willy: I learned reading and spelling. I can write my whole name . . . Willard George Arthur Witherspoon. *Pulls a piece of paper from his pocket and hands it to Sandy, proudly.*

Sandy: Is that really your name?

Willy: Uh huh, but mostly I'm called Willy. I like that better.

Sandy: Me too.

Willy: My mother still calls me Willard sometimes.

Sandy: Are you glad to be home and living with your mom again?

Willy: Yeah, only I don't think she likes me so well.

Sandy: Why not?

Willy: Because I'm not smart.

Sandy: Everyone can't be an Einstein.

Willy: What?

Sandy: Einstein. He's a real smart guy.

Willy: Does he go to your school?

Sandy: No, he's too old. Besides, I think he's dead.

Willy: That's too bad.

Sandy: It's okay. Lots of smart people are dead, but you're still alive. That makes you better than them, doesn't it?

Willy: I guess so.

Sandy: Besides, you're nice and that's better than smart.

Willy: I think you're nice . . . and smart.

Sandy: I'm not really so smart. I'm terrible at fractions.

Willy: What are fractions?

Sandy: Less than one of something. *She takes a peppermint stick out of her pocket and breaks it in half.* Like, if I have one peppermint stick and I break it in two, then we each have half. *She gives one half to Willy who stares at it.* That's fractions.

Willy: Candy cane.

Sandy: No, it's a peppermint stick. You can eat it.

Willy: It's a candy cane. For Christmas.

Sandy: What?

Willy: Christmas.

Sandy: Who's that?

Willy: Where I lived there was Christmas, but here it's gone.

Sandy: What's the matter, Willy? You look like you're going to cry. What do you mean by Christmas?

Willy: Christmas is everything beautiful. All glittery and happy and . . .

Alex: *From offstage.* Sandy!

Sandy: Oh, oh, it's my dad.

Alex walks into the street and spots Sandy and Willy. He comes over to them.

Alex: There you are. *Looks Willy up and down but talks only to*

Sandy. How would you like to run this down to the newspaper office for me?

Sandy: Right now?

Alex: Yes, right now. I want to get it in Monday's paper.

Sandy: *Taking the paper from him.* What is it?

Alex: It's a classified ad. We're putting the basement apartment up for rent.

Sandy: How come?

Alex: Times are tough. If we don't, you'll be going to school without shoes. Now get going.

Sandy: Aw!

Alex gives her a push in the appropriate direction.

Bye Willy.

She waves and goes off. When Sandy has gone, Alex directs his attention to Willy who is also trying to leave.

Alex: You must be Willy Witherspoon.

Willy: Yeah.

Alex: My name's Alex Kringle. I'm mayor of Split Hoof. *Shakes Willy's hand.* Sandy is my daughter. *Indicates the direction that Sandy went.* You two looked like you were having a good time. What were you talking about?

Willy: Christmas.

Alex: *Shocked.* What?

Willy: There isn't any Christmas here, Mr. Kringle. Back where I lived there was a Christmas tree already and lights and paper snowflakes and everything.

Alex: We don't cater to that nonsense here.

Willy: But it's nearly Christmas and there isn't any glitter in the windows or Christmas songs or anything.

Alex: *Controlling himself.* Willy, I don't think you should talk about Christmas to Sandy or anyone else, okay?

Willy: Why?

Alex: Because it wouldn't be a very good thing to do.

Willy: Why?

Alex: *Getting frustrated.* Because I said so.

Willy: But there should be Christmas trees and . . .

Alex: Willy, listen to me. *Slowly.* There is no Christmas in Split

Hoof. There hasn't been any Christmas here in ten years and it's better that way.

Willy: But there should be Christmas everywhere.

Alex: Not in Split Hoof.

Willy: But why?

Several Reasons for the Abolishment of Christmas
Alex:
Christmas
Got so ridiculous
That we meticulous -
Ly listed
Several reasons for its banning
At a meeting of the planning
Council for the propagation
Of the super-annuation,
Abolition, demolition,
Prohibition and sedition
Of the holly, mistletoeing
Jingle Bells and ho-ho-hoing!
So we held an anti-Christmas bylaw referendum.
The people of Split Hoof all agreed
That Christmas was precisely what we didn't need!

In Section 10, Subsection 7, Item 20, Clause 11
It's all here in black and white,
The answer to the plebiscite.
There shall be no Christmas in Split Hoof, EVER!!!

Willy: Why?

Alex: *Producing his bylaws.* Addendum.

Willy: A what-um?

Alex: Addendum!!! "Several Reasons for the Abolishment of Christmas".

You decorate distastefully,
And absolutely wastefully,
You chop a tree down shamelessly
And claim to do it blamelessly,
The needles drop perpetually,
The damned thing dies eventually,
Your carpet is then needlessly
With needles overcome.

To shop you must courageously
Fight crowds who act outrageously
The whole thing economically
Will cost you astronomically.
The bills come in eternally,
The interest mounts infernally,
You'll still be paying endlessly
The next millennium.

Christmas, it makes me furious,
But you're so curious,
I'll tell you just exactly how we planned it,
Just exactly why we banned it,
Why we held those reasons meetings,
Why we can't stand Season's Greetings!

The Carols play incessantly
And fill the air putrescently,
They're never played melodiously,
Or pleasantly, but odiously.
They crawl inside you hideously
To haunt your dreams insidiously,
They'll force you but dissentingly
To a sanatorium.

You shop for presents drudgingly
And only give them grudgingly,
They're just received ungraciously
Or just returned audaciously.
You grab your own gifts greedily
And rip them open speedily,
You'll drive each other finally to pandemonium!

Christmas, in its inanity,
Caused mass insanity
And harsh profanity.
Christmas has no validity,
It's pure stupidity.
It's just deplorably, revoltingly,
Detestably, repulsively,
Despicably, repugnantly,
Disgustingly, ridiculously,
DUMB!!!

Willy: DUMB?
Alex: Dumb!

The song ends. Alex is pleased with himself. Willy is confused.

Alex: There now, Willy. Now you understand why we can't have Christmas here, don't you?

Willy: *Hesitating.* I guess so.

Alex: Good. Now don't ever mention it again.

Alex exits. Willy stands for a moment and watches him go. He turns and speaks to himself.

Willy: *Softly.* But there ought to be Christmas.

The lights go down on the street.

Interlude

Mylar: Why? It sounds so horrible.

Willy: That's not really what it's like.

Willy rejoins Mylar to watch. Lectro enters with a towel over his head, lifts it up and looks at Mylar.

Lectro: Don't look at me. I'm not ready yet. *Leaves the stage.*

Mylar: This is weird.

Scene 3

The lights come up on the upstairs apartment. Pix is carefully hand-painting a china toy. Sandy comes in, taking off her coat as she does.

Sandy: I'm home.

Pix: Hang up your coat.

Sandy: Okay. *She hangs it on the doorknob. Pix has her back to her.*

Pix: And not on the doorknob.

Sandy: Do you have eyes in the back of your head?

Pix: Uh huh.

Sandy hangs up her coat. She leans on the back of Pix's chair.

Sandy: Pix, have you ever heard of something called Christmas?

Pix stiffens. She pauses to collect herself before she speaks.

Pix: Why do you ask that?

Sandy: I was just wondering. Willy started to tell me about it but I couldn't understand him too well.

Pix: Oh, you met Willy. *Pause.* I'm sure it wasn't anything important.

Sandy: But it sounded awfully important. More important than anything else. It almost made him cry.

Pix: Well Sandy, people like Willy get attached to strange things. Things that mean nothing to anyone else.

Sandy: Then you've never heard of Christmas?

Pix: Well . . . it's nothing you should be concerned about.

Sandy: But I am concerned or at least, curious. Tell me what you know about Christmas, Pix.

Pix: *Softly.* Christmas is a fantasy. *Catching herself.* It's a fantasy of Willy's. There is no Christmas.

Sandy: Willy says that there isn't any Christmas here, but there is where he used to live.

Pix: They humour the people who live in those institutions. There is no Christmas in Split Hoof. We live in the real world here.

Sandy: Then Christmas is only make-believe?

Pix: Yes, Christmas is make-believe.

Sandy: Like a fairy tale? Tell me the story of Christmas, Pix. *She sits down at Pix's feet. At this point Alex comes into the apartment. Pix throws the ornament she is painting onto the floor, pretending it was an accident.*

Pix: Oh! Butterfingers! Get a broom, Sandy . . . please. *Sandy gets up and goes out.* She's asking questions about Christmas.

Alex: *Shocked.* It's all the fault of that Willy Witherspoon. Have you told her anything?

Pix: I said it was a fantasy . . . like a fairy tale.

Alex: *Sarcastically.* Great!

Pix: Well, what was I supposed to tell her? She caught me by surprise.

Alex: I don't know.

Alex sinks into a chair. Sandy reappears with a broom and a dust pan. She sweeps up the broken pieces.

Sandy: Did you talk to Willy, Dad?

Alex: Yes.

Sandy: Didn't you like him? Wasn't he neat?

Alex: Did you give the ad to Mr. Richards?

Sandy: Yeah. He says it'll be in Monday's paper for sure.

Alex: Good.

Sandy: Willy told me that they have Christmas where he comes from. Pix was just going to tell me the story of Christmas, weren't you, Pix?

Pix: Well, I . . .

Alex: *Interrupting.* Isn't it time we started to think about supper?

Pix: Yes. What will we have for supper? There's some leftover casserole, or I could take something out of the freezer.

Alex: How about if I make a bunch of hamburgers. You always like that, don't you Sandy?

Sandy: What about Christmas?

Alex: *Laughing.* You can't eat that.

Sandy: I want to hear the story.

Pix: You're too old for stories.

Sandy: I am not.

Alex: Why don't you set the table?

Sandy: What's so secret about Christmas that nobody wants me to know about it? *Pause.*

Pix: It's just an old fairy tale.

Alex: It's better off forgotten.

Pix: Now go and set the table like a good girl.

Sandy gives them a look and then exits.

Alex: It's just an old fairy tale.

Lights go down on the apartment.

Interlude

Mylar: Hey, Pix! Why don't you just tell her.

Marzipan: Well . . . It's more complicated than that, Mylar.

Mylar: I thought you guys said "Simple is best".

Willy leaves his place with Mylar to join Sandy in Scene Four.

Scene 4

The lights come up on the barbershop. Sandy sneaks in then motions for Willy to follow her.

Willy: Are you sure your dad will let us play here?

Sandy: Sure, it's Sunday. The shop isn't open today.

Willy: Okay.

Sandy turns on a light switch. Sandy and Willy play with the barber paraphernalia. Sandy chases Willy with a barber's whisk, threatening to tickle him. She corners him in the barber chair.

Sandy: Now, tell me all about Christmas.

Willy: *Hesitating.* I can't.

Sandy: Why not?

Willy: Because your dad said no.

Sandy: My father told you not to say anything about Christmas?

Willy nods.

Sandy: Why?

Willy: He said it wouldn't be a good thing to do. He said lots of reasons, but I didn't understand any of them.

Sandy: There's something fishy going on. When I asked Dad and Pix about Christmas, they didn't want to talk about it.

Willy: My mother doesn't want to talk about it either, but she doesn't ever want to talk to me.

Sandy: Oh Willy, that's too bad. You've got me to talk to, though.

Willy: Yeah.

Sandy: So, talk to me about Christmas.

Willy hesitates and looks around cautiously. He leans forward as if to whisper to Sandy, then pauses and sighs.

Willy: I don't know how to start.

Sandy: Is it bigger than a bread box?

Willy: Christmas is exciting and fun.

Sandy: Like a carnival?

Willy: Sort of.

Sandy: Better than a carnival?

Willy: Yeah. Carnivals happen in the summer. Christmas comes in December when it's cold and Christmas makes everyone feel warm.

Sandy: Oh, Christmas is a chinook.

Willy: No. *Pause.* When Christmas comes, people have a Christmas tree.

Sandy: Christmas tree? I've never heard of a Christmas tree.

Willy: You make a Christmas tree out of a pine tree.

Sandy: How?

Willy: You put lights on it and balls and pretty things and when you're done it's so beautiful it makes you tingle inside.

Sandy: Tingle? *Willy nods.* Pix says that Christmas is a fairy tale.

Willy: It isn't a fairy tale. Christmas is real, but it glitters like a fairy tale. Everyone sends cards and gives presents and loves everyone, even the people they don't like the rest of the year.

Sandy: It sounds like a birthday party.

Willy: It is a birthday party . . . for the baby Jesus.

Sandy: Oh, Nativity!

Willy: Nativity?

Sandy: We call that Nativity. But all we ever do is go to church.

Willy: It's a wonderful party where you get presents from your parents and from Santa Claus if you've been good.

Sandy: Who is this Santa Claus? Does he live in Split Hoof?

Willy: No, he lives at the North Pole.

Sandy: No one lives at the North Pole. It's too cold.

Willy: Santa Claus does. He has a workshop there where he makes toys for all the good girls and boys.

Sandy: All the kids in the world?

Willy: Yup, he has elves who help him make the toys. They work all year round, then on Christmas eve Santa gets into his sleigh and delivers the toys all over the world.

Sandy: All in one night?

Willy: Yeah! He's got reindeer that fly.

Sandy: Flying reindeer?

Willy: Yeah. They're magic. There are eight of them and they all have names. There's Cupid and Vixen, Dasher, Blitzen, Dancer, Comet . . .

Sandy: That's only six.

Willy: There are two more, but I can't remember them. And THEN there's Rudolph!

Sandy: Another flying reindeer?

Willy: Yes, but his nose is red so the other reindeer won't play with him.

Sandy: Oh.

Willy: Only Santa makes them play with him because he likes Rudolph. Rudolph saved him once when he couldn't see in the fog.

Sandy: This is too weird. This Santa person who lives at the North Pole and makes toys and flies around on magic reindeer and gives everybody presents . . .

Willy: Yeah?

Sandy: What does he have to do with Christmas trees and loving people?

Willy: Santa loves everybody and he leaves presents under the Christmas tree if they're too big to go in your stocking.

Sandy: You mean if he's just got a little present for you he sticks it in your socks?

Willy: No, you leave a Christmas stocking out by the fireplace and Santa will fill it with candy.

Sandy: And you don't have to pay for it or anything?

Willy: No, you just leave him some milk and cookies. He gets pretty hungry flying all over the world.

Sandy: I guess. *Pause.* How does he get in the house?

Willy: He comes down the chimney.

Sandy: The chimney? *Pause.* What if you don't have a chimney?

Willy: He comes in by magic.

Sandy: Only never in Split Hoof.

Willy: When I was little he always came here.

Sandy: But why not now?

Willy: Your dad said that the people here don't want Christmas. They must have told Santa not to come any more.

Sandy: No one asked me if I wanted Christmas. I would have told Santa to come.

Willy: We could write him a letter.

Sandy: A letter to Santa Claus?

Willy: Yeah, telling him that we've been good and what we want for Christmas.

Sandy: What are we allowed to ask for?

Willy: Anything.

Sandy: And he'll bring it?

Willy: If you've been good.

Sandy: How good do you have to be?

Willy: Pretty good.

Sandy: What should we ask for?

Willy: A Christmas tree.

Sandy: I'd love to see a Christmas tree.

Willy: Then we'll ask Santa to bring us one.

Sandy: Just a second. I'll get some paper. *Scrambles around and finds a pencil and some paper.* Okay, what should we say?

Willy: Ask him how he is. *As Sandy writes, Willy encourages her.*

Dear Santa

Sandy:
Dear Santa
How are you?
How are all the elves?
And have they been working,
Have they behaved themselves?
How are Dasher, Dancer and Vixen,
Comet, Cupid and Blitzen,
And those other two, we forget their names,
Are they letting Rudolph join in their reindeer games?

Willy:
Santa, you will want to hear,
Dear Santa, how good we've been all year.
And Santa, could you find a way
To visit us on Christmas day?

Sandy:
Dear Santa
We promise
That if you come you'll find
Some milk and some cookies
Your very favourite kind.
We'll be waiting here for you Santa

Willy: Behaving here for you Santa.

Sandy: And there's just one gift we'd like to see,

Both: Dear Santa, could you bring us a Christmas tree?

Sandy:
Your friends,
Sandy and Willy.

Willy: That's me!

Song ends. Sandy folds the letter and puts it in the envelope.

Sandy: There. Do you know his address?

Willy: Santa Claus. North Pole.

Sandy: What street does he live on?

Willy: There aren't any streets at the North Pole.

Sandy: Okay, what's the postal code?

Willy: I don't think he has one.

Sandy: Then we just need a stamp.

Willy: No we don't.

Sandy: You just mail it like this?

Willy: Yeah.

Sandy: Doesn't Santa get mad that all his mail comes postage due?

Willy: I don't think it does.

Sandy: Boy, he must really be magic.

Willy: Come on, let's mail it.

Sandy: Okay.

They leave the barber shop and go out to the post box on the street. As they post the letter, Alex walks into the shop. We hear some strange music. The barber pole glows mysteriously and the mail box flies offstage. Sandy and Willy stare at this phenomenon open-mouthed. The lights go down on the street.

Interlude

Mylar is very taken with the flying mail box. She runs onto the stage.

Mylar: Hey great! I want to try that!

Sparkle: Later Mylar. Promise.

Mylar: Okay. *Returns to her seat with a renewed interest in the story as Scene Five begins.*

Scene 5

The lights come up on the upstairs apartment where Pix is trying to concentrate on making a toy while Alex paces the floor.

Alex: Things are getting out of control, Pix. They are definitely getting out of control.

Pix: Sit down Alex, you're going to wear a hole in the floor.

Alex: *Sits down for a second and then gets up and starts pacing again.* I've called every institution in the province and every one of them is stuffed to the gills. I couldn't even bribe any of them to take Willy.

Pix: Alex, you didn't try to bribe them, did you?

Alex: No, I didn't. But I would have if I thought it would do any good. Elvira is driving me crazy.

Pix: I'm sure you'll find some place sooner or later.

Alex: Sooner or later is going to be too late. Look at the trouble he's caused already. Sandy is asking embarrassing questions since Willy let it slip about Christmas.

Pix: Maybe we should tell her the truth, Alex.

Alex: The truth? Are you crazy? *Pause.* We're going to have to keep Sandy and Willy apart.

Pix: It's too late for that. You know Sandy—she'll never rest until she thinks she knows all about it.

Alex: Then we'll have to make up something to tell her.

Pix: I still think that the truth is the best thing.

Alex: And you want to reveal *all* the family secrets, is that it?! *Pause.* I think we should tell her that Christmas is a fairy tale, like you started to.

Pix: But Willy has already told her that there used to be Christmas in Split Hoof.

Alex: *Blurts.* We could tell her that Willy gets fairy tales and reality mixed up. *Pause.* Yes, we could.

Pix: All this stuff about Christmas all of a sudden makes me feel funny.

Alex: Well, forget about it. Everything has been peaceful and wonderful since we got rid of Christmas. You said so yourself.

Pix: I know, but when things start to get me down I think a little Christmas spirit wouldn't hurt!

Alex: You don't want to go back, do you?

Pix: No . . . No, I don't.

Alex: I'll talk to Sandy. I'll make her understand about Christmas. I might even tell her the truth.

Pix: Alex . . .

Alex: Not the whole truth, just about the referendum. Why we don't have Christmas. Why we don't *want* to have Christmas. *Alex exits. Pix is left alone a moment and then she sings.*

I Miss the Magic

Pix:
Wintertime,
Snow is falling down
Covering the town.

In wintertime,
Cold lies dark and deep,
Everything is sleeping.

Oh, I miss the magic—
To peer through frosted windowpanes,
Eat oranges and candy canes.
Oh, I miss the magic;
To build a friendship out of snow
And watch it come alive and grow.

Wintertime,
Frost hangs in the air,
Stillness everywhere,
In wintertime,
Silent echoes fall
Where songbirds once were calling.

Oh, I miss the magic—
When crackling fires cast out a glow
That warms the heart of all you know.
Oh, I miss the magic—
When stars shine brighter in the sky
And scientists can't tell us why.

Oh, I miss the magic—
When love surrounds us all because
There is a man called Santa Claus.

*She puts her work away, looks out the window, then exits as the
music finishes. The lights go down on the apartment.*

Interlude

*As the musical playout of "I Miss the Magic" continues, Mylar
comes on to the stage and she and Marzipan share a silent moment.
There is a growing understanding evident in the way Mylar is now
dealing with the other elves. She returns to her place to watch the
end of the act.*

Scene 6

The lights come up on the barber shop. Willy and Sandy enter, laden with bags full of Christmas decorations. Willy is somewhat hesitant.

Willy: I think your dad is going to be mad.

Sandy: He's mad lots of times.

Willy: But he's not going to like this.

Sandy: He won't stay mad.

They unpack the bags. They are full of all sorts of homemade Christmas decorations like paper chains, cutout snowflakes, drawings of snowmen and Santa Claus and slivers of aluminum foil icicles. They decorate the room as they talk.

Willy: But he doesn't like Christmas. He might hit me for telling you.

Sandy: I'll say it wasn't your fault. I'll say I made you tell me. After all, I did.

Willy: Then he'll hit you.

Sandy: Nah, he doesn't hit. He just doesn't give me my allowance or something.

Willy: My dad used to hit me.

Sandy: Does your mother?

Willy: No, she doesn't do anything.

Sandy: She's a weird lady. Hand me some more snowflakes.

Willy: *Hands her some decorations. Looking around.* It looks pretty.

Sandy: Yeah.

Willy: Do you think we should save some for the Christmas tree?

Sandy: What if Santa doesn't bring it?

Willy: He will. I know he will.

Sandy: I hope so, Willy.

Willy: He'll come.

Sandy: He never did before.

Willy: He'll come if you believe in him.

Sandy: I don't know. I couldn't find anything at the library about him.

Willy: Sandy, you *have* to believe in Christmas.

Sandy: I do. I think it's a wonderful idea. Winter needs a happy celebration. Everyone gets so grouchy in December, especially my dad.

Willy: When we get Christmas back, nobody will be grouchy.

Sandy: Really?

Willy: Uh huh. Come on, there's still more decorations.

Sandy: Okay. *Starts to decorate once more. Willy pulls a star from among the decorations.*

Willy: *Holding it up.* We'll save this for the top of the tree.

Sandy: A star.

Willy: *Looking around.* The barber shop is beautiful. Soon it'll be Christmas again.

Sandy: *With wonder.* Christmas. *Taking up a long paper chain.* Here, help me with this.

Alex walks into the shop and stares at the decorations.

Sandy: Surprise!

Alex: What on earth!?

Willy: Merry Christmas!

Alex: What do you two think you're doing?

Sandy: We're decorating the shop for Christmas!

Alex: There will be no Christmas in this town and particularly not in this shop. Now get rid of it.

Willy: But it looks so pretty.

Sandy: Willy and I made them ourselves.

Alex: I don't care if Michelangelo made them, take them down.

Willy: Michael who?

Sandy: Another smart guy who's dead.

Alex: Sandy . . .

Sandy: Daddy, you're not even trying to enjoy them.

Alex: Look. I've had about enough from you two. Christmas is a fairy tale.

Sandy: Willy says it's magic but it's real.

Alex: Willy can't tell reality from imagination.

Willy: I can too.

Alex: Christmas is a story made up by Clement Moore.

Willy: Who's that?

Sandy: I don't know, but I bet he was smart.

Willy: And dead?

Sandy: Likely.

Alex: He wrote a poem called "A Visit from St. Nicholas".

Sandy: Wait a minute. Who's St. Nicholas?

Willy: That's Santa Claus. He has lots of names. Santa Claus, St. Nicholas, Father Christmas, Kri . . .

Alex: Willy!

Sandy: This is too confusing to be a story. Stories are simple and the characters only have one name.

Alex: It's a legend that's gotten out of hand.

Sandy: But legends can sometimes be true.

Alex: Sandy, listen to me. I'm going to level with you.

Sandy: *Sceptical.* Really?

Alex: Christmas is a legend that some people believe and others don't. Clement Moore did write a poem that starts " 'Twas the night before Christmas" and that's where most people know the legend from. We celebrated Christmas in Split Hoof until ten years ago when the people of the town voted to ban Christmas.

Sandy: Why?

Alex: Because it's a nuisance.

Sandy: Why?

Music begins.

Several More Reasons for the Abolishment of Christmas

Alex:
Sandy, now try and understand
It just got out of hand.
That's why we had it banned.

Sandy: Why?

Willy: Addendum.

Sandy: A what-um?

Alex: Addendum! 'Several *more* reasons for the abolishment of Christmas.

You gulp your food down piggishly
And throw your drinks back swiggishly,
Your waistline automatically
Inflates and grows dramatically.
Your stomach, nauseatingly
Gives up regurgitatingly.

Your head will spin rotatingly
With one fat sugar plum.
Your relatives maliciously
Insult each other viciously.
They punish you vindictively
By hugging you constrictively.
And then they kiss rampageously
Thus spreading germs contagiously,
The phoniness unfailingly
Goes on ad nauseum.
Christmas caused mass hysterias,
Like rare malarias
From tropic areas.
Christmas just isn't sensible,
It's reprehensible,

It's just a
Topsy turvey, heebee geebee,
Hurley burley, mumbo jumbo,
Willy nilly, silliness
That's ipso facto
Absolutely
Dumb dumb dumb dumb dumb dumb dumb dumb
DUMB!

Sandy: Dumb?

Alex: Dumb.

Willy: Dumb?

Alex: Dumb.

Sandy/Willy: Dumb?

Alex: DUMB!

*As the song finishes, the barber shop door opens and John Smith
enters. He has a suitcase in one hand and a newspaper in the other.
The suitcase has many travel stickers on it. John Smith is thin,
clean shaven, and has short dark hair. The newspaper has a
classified ad circled.*

John: *To Sandy and Willy.* Hello. My name is John Smith.

Alex: Yes?

John: *Turning to him.* I've come about the apartment for rent. *He
points to the ad in the paper. He looks very nervous. As he and
Alex shake hands, Sandy and Willy look at this stranger. They all
freeze as the lights go to silhouette and the barber pole glows
mysteriously.*

Marzipan enters and leads a stunned Mylar from her seat for the intermission as "The Other Side of the Pole" theme ends the act.

Act 2
Interlude

Mylar: *Dragging Baubles onstage.* Come on Alex—you don't mind if I call you Al—we've got to get started. I want to see who this John Smith guy is.

Baubles: But it's not my scene.

Mylar: Sandy! Willy! Come on! We have to get started! *She drags Willy onstage.*

Willy: Lectro is on now.

Lectro has appeared and is doing a final check of his make-up. Willy leaves the stage. Lectro hands Mylar his mirror.

Lectro: Now you will see real acting.

Mylar: Far out.

Lectro takes his position for the top of Act Two as Mylar runs to her seat.

Scene 1

The lights come up on Sandy and Willy sneaking toward the window of the basement apartment. John Smith is in the basement apartment.

Willy: I don't think we should do this. It isn't right to spy on people.

Sandy: We're not really spying, we're detectives.

Willy: I don't feel like a detective.

Sandy: Here, put this on. *Hands him a deerstalker hat.*

Willy: Do I look like a detective now?

Sandy: The spitting image of Sherlock Holmes.

Willy: Is he another smart dead guy?

Sandy: No. He's a detective in a book and I'm Hercule Poirot. *Puts on a moustache.* Now, watch and see if he does anything suspicious. *Starts toward the window. Willy stops her.*

Willy: Where did you learn all these rules, Sandy?

Sandy: Hardy Boys and Nancy Drew books. They always sneak off and check out suspicious strangers. And they always manage to solve the mystery even though the grownups can't.

Willy: Are we going to solve a mystery, really?

Sandy: I don't know if there is a mystery, but if there is, we'll solve it. Now be very quiet and just watch. If he sees us, run like crazy, okay?

Willy: Okay.

They peer through the window as the lights come up full on the basement apartment. John Smith is there making himself at home. He puts his suitcase on the table and opens it. Out of the suitcase he brings all manner of large things that are obviously too big to fit in the suitcase. He also brings out some complicated looking radio equipment. As he does this he hums "Santa Claus is Coming to Town". When he has finished unpacking, he checks the doors and windows. As he approaches the window, Sandy and Willy duck. He doesn't see them. Satisfied that the coast is clear, he sits down to send a radio message.

John: This is Kris calling Crumhorn. Come in Crumhorn. This is Kris calling Crumhorn. Do you read me?

Voice: This is Crumhorn. We read you loud and clear.

John: Roger, Crumhorn. I've arrived safely in Split Hoof. No one is suspicious so far. How are things at your end?

Voice: Slow as ever, Kris. We anticipate no problems. Everything should be ready for zero hour.

John: Good. I'm going to begin investigations immediately. I'll return as soon as I've found Pix. Meanwhile I'll keep you posted.

Voice: Roger, Kris. Good luck.

John: Thanks Crumhorn. And Crumhorn . . . Alex is here.

Voice: *Pause.* I read you Kris. Over and out.

The lights fade on John Smith and come up bright on Sandy and Willy in the street.

Willy: Wow!

Sandy: Something fishy is going on here.

Willy: Do you think he's a crook?

Sandy: More likely a spy. But what does he want in Split Hoof and why does he want to find Pix?

Willy: Is he going to hurt her?

Sandy: I don't know. Spies are pretty ruthless usually.

Willy: Do you really think he's a spy? A real live spy?

Sandy: What else could he be? *Pause while she thinks of all the terrible things he could be.* Okay, Willy, calm down. I'm going to question Pix, subtly of course. You stay here and watch the spy. We're going to foil his plans, whatever they are.

Willy: Right!

Willy settles down by the window and peers in. The lights fade on him as Sandy exits.

Mylar joins Willy watching at the window. She is deadly earnest about the action which is unfolding. She remains with Willy all through Scene. Two.

Scene 2

The lights come up on the upstairs apartment. Pix is making a rag doll. Sandy enters.

Sandy: Hi, Pix.

Pix: I didn't expect you back so soon.

Sandy: There's nothing to do outside.

Pix: What's the moustache for?

Sandy suddenly realizes that she is still in disguise. She takes off the moustache and hides it.

Sandy: Ah, nothing. Willy and I were just playing.

Pix: I hope you don't get too attached to Willy. You know he's going to be leaving soon.

Sandy: Has Daddy found an institution for him?

Pix: Not yet, but it's only a matter of time.

Sandy: Oh. *Pause.* What are you making?

Pix: A rag doll. *Holds up the doll.* Do you like her?

Sandy: She's nice.

Pix: Here, help me cut the wool for her hair. *Hands Sandy a ball of orange wool and some scissors.*

Sandy: Pix, I was just thinking. I really don't know anything about you.

Pix: What do you mean, you don't know anything about me?

Sandy: You told me that you came to Split Hoof, fell in love with Daddy, got married and had me, but what about before that? Where did you live before you came to Split Hoof?

Pix: A little place north of here.

Sandy: What's it called?

Pix: You wouldn't have heard of it.

Sandy: I don't care. Tell me.

Pix: *Pause.* It's called Olpay. North Olpay.

Sandy: Olpay. What a weird name.

Pix: I told you you wouldn't have heard of it.

Sandy: Does your family still live there?

Pix: I haven't got any family.

Sandy: Were they all killed by vicious murderers?

Pix: Sandy! Don't be ridiculous.

Pause.

Sandy: What do you think of the name Crumhorn?

Pix: *Startled by the mention of the name.* Crumhorn?

Sandy: For the doll. Don't you think it's a nice name?

Pix: It's rather an odd name for a doll.

Sandy: I was going to call it KRIS, but I think Crumhorn is better.

Sandy is carefully watching Pix who is maintaining control remarkably well. They finish with the doll's hair and Sandy pockets the rest of the ball of wool. She wanders around the room trying to think of her next tactic. She picks up a mystery novel and plops down in a chair.

Sandy: This book is really interesting.

Pix: Is it?

Sandy: Yeah. It's called 'The Mystery of the Hoodoo Hooligans'. It's about spies. Spies lead very exciting lives.

Pix: I imagine.

Sandy: Have you ever known a spy?

Pix: Not that I know of.

Sandy: But you might have known a spy and not known it?

Pix: Sandy . . . really.

Sandy: Sorry, it's the book. It's easy to get caught up in the kind of life a spy leads.

Pix: I think you should go down to the library and get some proper story books.

Sandy: I hate library books. They always have pages missing. Besides, I promised I'd meet Willy, right about now. *Sandy secures the house, puts on her moustache, picks up her coat and charges out.*

Pix: *As Sandy leaves.* Don't be late for supper! *After a moment.* Kris? Crumhorn?

The lights go out on the upstairs apartment.

Interlude

Mylar runs to Marzipan.

Mylar: Pix, be careful; there's a strange man in your basement!

Marzipan: Exciting isn't it!

Mylar: OOOOOOhhhh. *Sits down in her seat again with obvious trepidation for Scene Three.*

Scene 3

The lights come up on Willy peering through the basement window. Sandy enters.

Sandy: Did you find out anything?

Willy: He's just been sitting there with his feet up looking at a long piece of paper with names on it. It must be important. He checked it twice.

Sandy: Pix looked as if she recognized the names Kris and Crumhorn, but I couldn't get anything out of her.

Willy: I think we should call the police.

Sandy: We can't call the police. When it comes to mysteries, the police are useless.

Willy: Oh.

Sandy: I think we're going to have to do something drastic if we're going to crack this case.

Willy: Like what?

Sandy: We'll use this! *Pulls the ball of wool from her pocket.*

Willy: That's pretty. Are you going to make some mittens?

Sandy: No, we're going to tie up the crook with this yarn and then torture the information out of him.

Willy: I've never tortured anyone before.

Sandy: It's easy. I've read all about it. Then, after we torture him, we solve the mystery and the police will give us a citation.

Willy: What's a citation?

Sandy: I think it's a car!

Willy: Wow!

Sandy: We can use the element of surprise to our advantage. He won't be expecting an all-out assault so soon.

Willy: So we knock on the door and yell "Surprise!"?

Sandy: No. We knock on the door and make up some kind of a story.

Willy: I know a story about a princess.

Sandy: Not that kind of story. I'll tell him we're collecting for some strange group or another.

Willy: What do I do?

Sandy: I'll start talking to him and, when I give the signal, you jump on him and tie him up, okay? *Hands Willy the ball of wool.*

Willy: Okay.

Sandy: The signal will be when I scratch my nose.

Willy: When you scratch your nose, I jump on him?

Sandy: Right. Here goes.

They approach the door. Sandy knocks. John opens the door immediately. Sandy stutters for a second.

John: Yes?

Sandy: Good afternoon, Sir. We're collecting for . . . SPORT, the Society for the Preservation of Rabid Tarantulas. Would you care to give something?

John: Rabid tarantulas . . . my word.

Sandy: It's a very worthy cause. *Scratches her nose. Willy is not paying attention.*

John: Yes, I'm sure it is. *Sandy scratches her nose again.*

Sandy: You have no idea how downtrodden and abused the tarantulas are, and they're practically extinct. *Scratches her nose furiously. John offers her a handkerchief.*

Sandy: *In a stage whisper.* Willy.

Willy: What?

She gives him a dirty look and scratches her nose.

Willy: Oh. *Leaps forward and picks John up. He carries him to a chair.*

John: Hey!

Sandy: Sit on him, Willy. Don't let him get away.

Willy sits on John's lap.

John: What's the meaning of this?

Sandy: Now tie him up.

Willy hands John the end of the ball of wool and starts tying him up by running around the chair.

Sandy: Your reign of terror is over, Kris! We know who you are.

John: You do?

Willy: Yes, you're a crook.

Kris: Wait a minute . . .

Sandy: Quiet. You're not supposed to say anything until we start to torture you.

Kris: Torture?

Willy: That's right.

Kris: Remind me to take you off my nice list and put you onto naughty.

Willy: What's he talking about?

Sandy: I think it's code.

Kris: Untie me. I promise I won't run away.

Sandy: That's what they all say.

Willy: We have to torture you now.

Sandy: We interrogate him first, Willy.

Willy: Oh, right.

Sandy: You search the place while I question the crook.

Willy: Right.

Willy starts searching the apartment. Through the next segment Kris is trying to divide his attention between Sandy's questioning and Willy's searching.

Sandy: Okay, Kris, where were you on the night of February 31st?

Kris: There is no February 31st.

Sandy: Ah ha! So you stole that too, did you?

Kris: Ho-ho-hold on a minute.

Sandy: See Willy, he's starting to crack under the pressure already.

Willy: Is he?

Sandy: Who were you with on the night in question?

Kris: I was alone.

Sandy: Do you have witnesses?

Kris: Witnesses?

Willy: It means people who saw you do it.

Kris: Do what?

Sandy: What does the name Crumhorn mean to you?

Kris: How do you know about Crumhorn?

Sandy: We ask the questions, not you.

Willy: Sandy! Look what I found. A disguise. *Holds up a fake white beard. Sandy rushes over to examine it.*

Sandy: Let's see what we've got here.

Sandy takes the beard from Willy and tries it on. Meanwhile, Willy has pulled a red suit out of the bag. She holds that up to herself as well.

Willy: You look just like Santa Claus. *Suddenly realizing what this means.* That's Santa's suit.

Willy/Sandy: *Point at Kris.* What have you done with Santa?

Kris: I am Santa.

Sandy: A likely story.

Kris: It's true.

Sandy: Prove it.

Kris: Ho Ho Ho.

Sandy: Unconvincing.

Kris: Well, you might recognize this then. *Takes their letter out of his pocket and hands it to them.*

Willy: It's the letter we sent.

Sandy: Let me see.

Kris: And by the way, the other two reindeer are Prancer and Donder.

Sandy: This doesn't prove anything. You could have stolen this.

The radio suddenly crackles to life. Kris removes the wool from around him.

Don't anybody move.

Voice: This is Crumhorn calling Kris. Come in Kris. This is Crumhorn calling Kris. Do you read me?

Kris: Excuse me. *Goes to the radio. Willy and Sandy make no attempt to stop him.*

Kris: This is Kris. I read you loud and clear, Crumhorn.

Voice: Roger Kris. Can you come back to the North Pole immediately? We have a bit of a problem here.

Kris: But I just got here.

Voice: I know, but it's an emergency. We just got a surprise order for five thousand wooden building blocks. We'll never get them ready in time.

Kris: Just give me a few more days.

Voice: Can't Kris. You know how short-handed we are. There are only five of us left. I'll be sending Rudolph to get you as soon as possible.

Kris: Crumhorn . . .

Voice: No time to talk Kris. It's incredibly busy up here. You know how crazy things can get this close to Christmas, even these days.

Kris: I know, but . . .

Voice: See you, Kris. Over and out. *Pause.*

Sandy: *In awe.* You really are Santa Claus.

Kris: That's right.

Sandy: *To Willy.* That's not what you said Santa Claus looked like.

Kris: I'm in disguise.

Sandy: If you're Santa Claus, why does everyone call you Kris?

Willy: Kris Kringle. That's another one of Santa's names.

Kris: That's right.

Sandy: Kringle? That's my last name.

Kris: And Alex Kringle is your father?

Sandy: Yeah.

Kris: *With emotion.* That makes me your . . . grandfather.

Sandy: Grandfather?

Willy: Santa's your grampa!

Sandy: *In awe.* I don't believe it. My dad is Santa's son?

Kris: I've got a granddaughter.

Willy: Don't just stand there. You're supposed to hug each other.

Kris: Ho, Ho, Ho. *They embrace.*

Sandy: Wait till Pix hears about this.

Kris: Pix? You know Pix?

Sandy: She's my mother.

Kris: Then she's all right! Ho! Ho! Ho!

Willy: Is Pix a friend of yours?

Kris: She was my best elf.

Sandy: Pix was an elf?

Kris: The best one I ever had, till she left to look for your father.

Willy: Was he lost?

Kris: We had a misunderstanding. We said some things we shouldn't have. Then he left.

Sandy: And Pix went to bring him back?

Kris: All the elves went out to find him. Pix never returned. I've been worried.

Willy: I can't believe that Pix is an elf. She's too big to be an elf.

Kris: Elves aren't really like they show them in books. They aren't tiny and they don't have pointy ears or anything.

Willy: Do they wear pointed hats and shoes that curl up at the toes?

Kris: Some do, some don't. Elves are individuals. They pick their own styles. Crumhorn, for example, likes to wear tie-dyed T-shirts and a French beret.

Sandy: Weird.

Willy: It'd be neat to be an elf.

Sandy: Pix doesn't know you're here, does she?

Kris: Not yet.

Sandy: Does Daddy?

Kris: No, he didn't recognize me.

Willy: Do you want us to tell them?

Kris: I don't know.

Sandy: What do you mean, you don't know?

Kris: I just wanted to make sure that Pix was safe. I'd like to see both her and Alex, but I don't think they'd want to see me.

Willy: Sure they do. Everyone wants to see Santa.

Kris: Oh, Willy, I wish that were true, but fewer and fewer people want to believe in me any more.

Willy: I believe in you.

Sandy: So do I.

Dear Santa *(Reprise)*

Kris:
I know you do and yet it's true,
Not everyone believes like you,
And so the answer I have drawn
There seems no point in going on.

The world is trying to destroy
What still remains of yuletide joy.
There's now so little Christmas cheer
That this must be my final year.

Willy: Santa, you can't give up Christmas!

Kris: But Willy, almost everyone else in the world has.

Sandy: But we haven't! We've just started!

Kris: Oh, Sandy . . .

Sandy:
Oh dear Santa please,
Whatever you do,
Dear Santa please believe that
We still love you.

We'll be your friends
Sandy and Willy . . .

Kris: That's true. *Laughs.* I'm a foolish old man.

Sandy: What do you mean?

Kris: That I'm foolish enough to be thinking of giving up Christmas when there are still Sandies and Willies in this world.

Sandy: I'll bring Pix to see you. I'm sure she'll want to! *Runs out.*

Kris: *Calling after her.* Sandy, I . . . I don't know! *Turns to Willy as the lights go down on the basement apartment.*

Interlude

Mylar comes on stage and presents herself to Lectro. She is beginning to understand what the point of the story is. Lectro, as Kris, invites her to join with Willy as he tells them a story.

Lectro: Come on. I'll tell you a little story.

Mylar remains as Scene Four begins.

Scene 4

The lights come up on the upstairs apartment. Pix is, of course, making some kind of toy. Sandy bursts in.

Sandy: Pix! Pix! Pix! Come quick! Mr. Smith is sick.

Pix: What?

Sandy: Mr. Smith, the man who rented the apartment. He's really sick. He asked me to come and get you.

Pix: Oh dear. Maybe we should call an ambulance.

Sandy: No! He said he won't go to a hospital. He's afraid of doctors.

Pix: If he's sick he should get professional care.

Sandy: Well, you tell him that.

Pix: All right.

Pix follows Sandy through the barber shop to the basement apartment. Kris is telling Willy a story. Mylar is with them.

Kris: And I heard him exclaim as he rose out of sight, "Happy Christmas to all and to all a good night!" Ho! Ho! Ho!

Mylar: Far out.

Willy: That's a good story, Santa!

Kris: Well, it's *my* favourite.

There is a knock. Lectro gives Mylar the nose she will use later. She returns to her seat. Pix and Sandy enter.

Kris: Oh Sandy, come in. I was just telling Willy a story. Who's this you've brought with you?

Pix: Excuse me, Mr. Smith. Sandy said you were ill. Is there anything I can do?

Kris: Ill? I've never felt fitter in my life.

Pix: But . . .

Kris: Sandy, I didn't want you to lie to her. It isn't nice to lie.

Pix: Lie? . . . I'm terribly sorry for disturbing you. Come on, Sandy.

Kris: Pix.

Pix: *Hesitates, then* . . . Kris?

Kris: It's me.

Pix: But Kris, what happened to your beard? And you're so thin . .

Kris: I shaved, dyed my hair . . . joined weight watchers . . . What's the matter? Don't you like the new me?

Pix: What are you doing here, Kris?

Kris: I came to find you.

Pix: And take me back to the North Pole?

Kris: Not if you didn't want to go.

Pix: I don't want to go.

Kris: All right.

Pix: That's not what you wanted to hear, was it?

Kris: Pix, I've been worried about you. I've been trying to get into Split Hoof for ten years. I wanted to make sure you were all right.

Pix: I've been happy, Kris. I like life without Christmas.

Kris: Do you?

Pix: Of course I do.

Kris: Sandy tells me that you're always making toys and that you like her to call you by your elfin name. Once an elf always an elf, Pix?

Pix: I suppose you know that Alex is here, *Kris nods.* and that we're married.

Kris: Yes. *Looks at Sandy. Pause.*

Pix: I think you should leave before he finds out that you're here. *Turns to go.*

Kris: Pix, I need your help. I want to bring Christmas back to Split Hoof. Willy and Sandy and I do. You've got to help us.

Pix: Split Hoof manages quite well without Christmas.

Kris: Please Pix, try to remember the good times.

Pix: The good times happened when there wasn't any Christmas.

Sandy: Didn't you like the lights on the Christmas trees?

Willy: Jingle Bells and turkey dinner?

Kris: The extra specialness of Christmas love?

Pix: Kris I . . . *Throws her arms around him and starts to cry.*

Kris: It's okay Pix. It's okay.

Pix: I do miss the magic, Kris. Sometimes I miss it so much I think I'll die if I never see another Christmas tree. And I dream about it. About going back to the North Pole with Crumhorn and all the other elves. About singing in the workshop. About sneaking out to feed carrots to Rudolph.

Kris: Ah, Rudolph.

Pix: Is he just the same?

Kris: Just the same. He hasn't changed a bit since the time Alex came home pulling him by a rope and yelling out "He followed me home, can I keep him?"

They all laugh for a few seconds, then there is a silence.

Pix: What are you going to do about Alex?

Kris: I don't know. Nothing I guess. I don't think he'll talk to me and Rudolph will be here for me soon.

Sandy: You're not going to give up just like that, are you?

Willy: I thought we were going to bring Christmas back.

Pix: That's more difficult than you think, Willy. The people of Split Hoof don't want Christmas.

Sandy: Especially not Daddy, right?

Willy: *Pause.* You should talk to Mr. Kringle, Santa. You could convince him to bring Christmas back.

Kris: I would like to bring Christmas back, but as far as talking to Alex . . . I don't know. I'm afraid.

Sandy: Afraid of what?

Kris: Of failing. If I can't convince my own son to believe in Christmas, how can I expect anyone else to believe?

Sandy: I believe in Christmas.

Willy: Me too.

Pix: And me . . . Talk to him, Kris. It's worth a try.

Kris nods and the lights fade.

Interlude

Mylar: *Jumps up.* Right. You tell him Kris!

The other elves acknowledge her enthusiasm and head off to set the next scene. Mylar, however, is insistent.

I mean, if you don't talk to him, he'll never find out about Christmas and . . . well . . .

Where

Mylar:

Christmas isn't easy to find.

Christmas is a state of mind.

You might think that you can see it.

Willy: You might think that "that" must be it,

Mylar:

But Christmas is a thing of a rather different kind.

Christmas isn't something you hold.

Christmas isn't young or old.

Eyes and ears just won't reveal it.

Willy: You can only really feel it,

Mylar:

For Christmas lives in hearts that are made of solid gold.

So put away your directories,

Your maps, your charts,

Your things like these.

To find it

Why not try . . .

To hang a Christmas stocking up beside the fire.

Sing your favourite carol with Yuletide choir.

Willy:
Though that might be pleasant
There's a very special present
And it's something that we all desire.

Mylar:
Sneak a peek in packages beneath the tree.
You might even ask for it on Santa's knee.
You might have an inkling
That it's where bright lights are twinkling,

Willy/Mylar: But it might be rather hard to see.

Mylar: Steal a kiss or two beneath the mistletoe,

Willy: Or rub noses with a friendly Eskimo.

Mylar:
There's a famous carol
Where you don your gay apparel,

Willy/Mylar: But will that set Christmas hearts a-glow?

Willy: Hang a wreath of holly up on every door.

Mylar: Eat a pound of chocolates

Willy: And then eat ten more.

Mylar: Hear the sleigh-bells jingle,

Willy:
You might feel a certain tingle,
But is that what you are looking for?

The other elves leave the stage as Baubles enters to prepare for his next scene. Willy and Mylar include him in the song.

Willy/Mylar:
You might think it's hiding underneath the snow.
You might think it's wrapped up in a satin bow.

Willy: Look in children's faces

Mylar: And a million other places . . .

Willy/Mylar: But unless you look, you'll never know.

Mylar and Willy encourage Baubles in his preparation for the dramatic scene and then return to their places to watch.

Scene 5

The lights come up on Alex in the barber shop reading a newspaper. The door from the basement apartment opens and Kris enters.

Alex: Ah, Mr. Smith. Is everything all right in your little apartment?

Kris: Just fine, Mr. Kringle. Just fine.

Alex: Good. What can I do for you?

Kris: Oh. *Hesitates.* I thought I'd have a shave.

Alex: A shave. Okay. Just sit down right here.

Kris sits and Alex covers him with a barber's apron and prepares some hot towels for Kris' face.

Alex: So, how do you like Split Hoof, Mr. Smith?

Kris: Just fine. Lovely little town you've got here. I understand you're the mayor.

Alex: That's right. I've been the mayor for ten years. Hardly seems that long, you know. How time flies.

Kris: It certainly does.

Alex: *Moves behind Kris, mixing shaving cream in a mug.* So tell me, Mr. Smith, what do you do for a living?

Kris: I'm in the toy business.

Alex: Really. How is business doing?

Kris: Not so good right now. I thought I'd be able to help it along by coming here.

Alex: Are you thinking of setting up a factory here?

Kris: No, I'm more interested in the folks who make handcrafted toys.

Alex: You should talk to my wife. She's forever making one thing or another. We've got so many toys in the house, we don't know what to do with them.

Kris: I'd like to see those toys. I'm always interested in new ideas for handcrafted toys.

Alex: Which you'll have made in Japan, no doubt.

Kris: Well, perhaps a little bit north of Japan.

Alex starts lathering Kris' face. By the time he is finished it should look as if Kris has a big white beard.

Alex: Thinking of staying permanently in Split Hoof?

Kris: I don't know yet.

Alex: It's a great town if you don't mind a few eccentric citizens.

Kris: Oh?

Alex: Take Elvira Witherspoon for example. She's a very strange lady on the town council. She just introduced a bill to restrict admittance to the zoo to people over 18. She claimed that a monkey did something very rude right in front of her. She was most offended.

Alex begins to laugh and Kris joins in. After Alex stops, Kris is still laughing.

Kris: Ho, ho, ho . . . .

Alex looks at Kris' lather covered face and recognizes him.

Kris: Hello Alex.

Alex: What are you doing here? Spying on me?

Kris: I'm not spying on you.

Alex: Then why did you come to Split Hoof, and in disguise, no less?

Kris: I came here to look for Pix.

Alex: She's been here for ten years.

Kris: I know that. I sent her here . . . to look for you.

Alex: What made you think that I was here?

Kris: I didn't. I sent my elves out all over the world looking for you. Pix is the only one who didn't come back. I thought she might have been the victim of foul play.

Alex: And was she?

Kris: Don't Alex.

Alex: It took you long enough to get here.

Kris: You know as well as I do that if no one in a town believes in me, I can't get in. Split Hoof has been sealed off for ten years.

Alex: How come you're here now?

Kris: Someone believes.

Alex: That infernal Willy, no doubt.

Kris: Yes, and Sandy.

Alex: What do you want from me, Dad?

Kris: I want you to let Christmas back into Split Hoof, Alex.

Alex: No! I hate Christmas! I hate it more than anything else.

Kris: Alex . . .

Alex: You don't know what it was like for me, Dad! For every other child in the world, Christmas was a magical family time.

Kris: Christmas is the busiest time of the year for me. I'm sorry if I . . .

Alex: It's too late to be sorry. I hated Christmas time. All the other guys at boarding school would talk about Christmas trees, carol singing, turkey dinners. What did I get? Peanut butter sandwiches for Christmas dinner.

Kris: I gave you toys . . . I . . .

Alex: Do you think I wanted toys? I spent my whole life surrounded by toys.

Kris: Giving toys was the only way I knew of showing love.

Alex: All I wanted was a home, a warm loving home; I have one now. Now that there isn't any Christmas.

Kris: Don't blame Christmas.

Alex: Don't blame Christmas? You have no idea how hard it was being your son. The other kids laughed at me when I said that Santa Claus was my father. They didn't even believe in Santa. Well, I don't believe any more, either.

Kris: And that's what frightens me, Alex. Look at me. Look at how thin I've gotten. I say it's because I've been on a diet, but that isn't true. It's because fewer and fewer people are believing in me. Alex, if everyone stops believing, what will happen to me?

Alex: You never stopped to think what happened to me.

Kris: Yes I did. I looked for you for years. After so much time, I gave up hope.

Alex: You didn't check the headquarters of ABC.

Kris: ABC?

Alex: The Association for the Banishment of Christmas.

Kris: Oh yes, them.

Alex: I joined up with them. They hate Christmas almost as much as I do.

Kris: I know about ABC and the way they work. They investigate places with some anti-Christmas feeling and then send someone in to finish the job.

Alex: Abolishing Christmas in Split Hoof was easy. Elvira Witherspoon had paved the way nicely for me. Anti-Christmas feeling was running high. All it took was a little push from Elvira and me to send it over the edge.

Kris: And deprive your own daughter of Christmas joy.

Alex: You deprived your son.

Kris: Alex, I'm sorry that I didn't realize what I was doing to you, but think of Sandy. Don't make her go through the same thing.

Alex: She doesn't know what she's missing.

Kris: But she knows now.

Alex: She thinks that Santa Claus is the figment of some writer's imagination.

Kris: No she doesn't.

Alex: I told her Christmas wasn't real and she has no reason not to believe me.

Kris: Yes she does. She's met me.

Alex: Why couldn't you just leave us alone?

Kris: Sandy is my granddaughter. Besides, she was the one who couldn't leave me alone.

Alex: What do you mean by that?

Kris: She and Willy attacked me and tied me up. Ho, ho, ho. They thought I was a crook.

Alex: They weren't far wrong.

Kris: How many times do I have to say I'm sorry?

Alex: Does it matter? *Pause.*

Kris: What about Sandy? What are you going to tell her and Willy?

Alex: Willy's going off to an institution as soon as I can find one for him.

Kris: I could suggest a nice sheltered workshop where Willy could live.

Alex: Goodbye Dad.

Kris: And Sandy?

Alex: She'll forget about Christmas soon enough.

Kris: I don't think she will.

Alex: I don't want to hear any more.

Kris: Okay . . . I guess I'll be going. Rudolph will be here for me any time now.

Alex: Rudolph? . . . How is Rudolph?

Kris: He's fine.

Alex turns away. Kris looks at him for a second then goes for the door.

Kris: Merry Christmas, Alex.

Kris exits. Alex is left alone onstage, almost decides to follow Kris, hesitates, takes a moment for reflection and then sings.

Once

Alex:
Once I was a winter child,
Born of ice and snow
The northern lights, how they smiled on me.
A warming living glow.
A sky of diamond brightness
Reflected down below
The crystal whiteness
Of the home I used to know.

As Alex starts his second verse, we see Kris enter his apartment and begin to pack. He will also set out paper and pen and write a short note.

But once I was a winter storm,
Raging at the land
With icy fury that the warmest heart
Could not withstand.
As harsh as northern winds can blow,
As cruel as biting frost,
My anger lay like deepest snow
Until my home was lost.

Once I was a winter bird,
Born to own the sky,
I found my wings when I heard a call
That told me I must fly.
The midnight sun that I fled from
No longer smiles for me.
I flew to freedom
But am I really free?

Lights come up full on Kris contemplating his letter. He sings.

Kris:
Dear Sandy and Willy,
There's something I must say.
The time has come
For me to go away.

Once a magic filled the air
A warming, living glow,
A time of loving and caring that
Could melt the cruelest snow.
But winter nights are cold now,

The warmth has all expired,
And I am old now,
I'm old and very tired.

Alex repeats the first verse quietly while Kris sings.

Though so very few believe,
My burden is not light,
For without love, Christmas Eve is just
Another lonely night.
There seems no point, no reason,
No use in going on,
Just this last season,
And then I will be gone.

Promise me
You'll always be
My friends, Sandy and Willy.

Alex:
Was it so
Long ago?
I have freedom now
But am I really free?

The lights fade on both areas.

Willy sends Mylar out of the auditorium as he takes his place for Scene Six.

Scene 6

Kris is standing in the street with his suitcase at his side watching the skies for Rudolph's arrival. Sandy, Willy and Pix enter and see him prepared for departure. Sandy joins him.

Sandy: Is Rudolph here yet?

Kris: Not yet.

Willy: *Joins them.* Are you going to put on your red suit to ride in the sleigh, Santa?

Kris: I don't think so.

Sandy: Why not? Then everyone would know that you're Santa Claus.

Kris: That isn't a very popular thing to be around here.

Sandy: Come on Santa, where's your Christmas spirit?

Willy: I think you'd feel better if you wore the suit.

Pix: *Joining them.* He's probably right, Kris.

Kris: All right. *Opens the suitcase and takes out the red suit. They help him put on the pants. They are miles too big for him.*

Sandy: Are you sure these are yours?

Kris: *Defensively.* Well, I have lost a bit of weight.

Pix: You're the most pitiful looking Santa I've ever seen.

Willy: He only needs some pillows.

Kris: *To Pix.* Yes, I only need some pillows.

Sandy: I'll go get some.

She rushes off into the house to get some pillows. Pix and Willy help him on with the beard, cap and jacket.

Kris: *As he puts the beard on.* Ho, ho, ho, that tickles!

Sandy: *Returns.* Here are the pillows!

Sandy and Willy stuff the back, Pix stuffs the front. They fluff the pillows.

Kris: Ho, ho, ho, be careful. There should be a belt in that suitcase.

Willy finds it. As it is enormous, he wraps it around Kris the same way he did with the wool, by running around him.

Kris: *Watching him.* You're pretty good at wrap-around tying, aren't you?

Willy, Sandy and Pix stand back to admire the effect.

Sandy: There, that's better.

Willy: You really look like Santa, now.

Kris: I wish I felt like Santa.

Pix: I guess your talk with Alex didn't go very well, huh?

Kris: *Sullen.* No.

Pix: Oh Kris, I'd hoped things would turn out better.

Willy: Does this mean we're never going to have Christmas here?

Sandy: Oh Willy, don't say that.

The sound of sleigh bells is heard offstage.

Kris: *Points up.* Look, here comes Rudolph and he's brought your Christmas present, too.

Mylar enters dressed as Rudolph, carrying a fully decorated Christmas tree onto the stage.

Mylar: *To the audience.* It's really me!

Sandy: Oh Santa . . . it's beautiful.

Willy: It's the most beautiful Christmas tree I've ever seen.

Sandy: Where's our star, Willy?

Willy: *As Mylar hands it to him.* Here.

Kris: No Christmas tree is complete without a star.

Sandy takes the star and with Willy's help puts it on top of the tree.

A star. Just like the one in the first Christmas.

Pix: *Knowingly.* Tell us the story, Kris.

Kris: Well . . . all right. It goes like this . . .

The Song of the Star

Kris: Once upon a time, a long time ago in a land far away from here . . .

Sings.

Men upon a hill
Were resting for the night,
When suddenly a thrill
Went through them.

In the sky above
There shined a dazzling light,
A messenger of love
Came to them.

Pix joins him to sing.

Pix/Kris:
He told the wondrous story
Of how the star so shined.
He told them of the glory
They would find.
He sang of joy, hope, love
For mankind.

Pix:
Wise men from afar
Looked out upon the night,
And there they saw the star-
Light gleaming.

Radiant and strong,
It was the perfect light
Of which they had so long
Been dreaming.

Pix/Kris:
So westward they went riding
To where the starlight shined,
Its brilliance ever guiding them
To find

Sandy/Willy/Rudolph:
The light of joy, hope, love
For mankind.

Alex enters unseen by the others.

Kris:
Light was streaming down
Upon a scene of joy,
Within a humble town
They found Him.

Pix:
In a lowly stall
There slept a tiny Boy
But radiance was all
Around Him.

Pix sees Alex and stops singing.

Alex: I'd forgotten about that story.

Pix: Alex.

Kris: *Embarrassed.* We all forget too often.

Alex: I saw Rudolph. He landed right in the middle of 50th Street.

Kris: I suppose I shouldn't keep him waiting. *Picks up his suitcase. Alex looks at the tree.*

Alex: I'd forgotten how beautiful a Christmas tree could be . . . I suppose it's my turn to say I'm sorry, isn't it, Dad?

Kris: We've been stupid, both you and I.

Alex: Yeah . . . I'm sorry about ABC. I shouldn't have done what I did.

Kris: And I shouldn't have been so blind to your unhappiness.

Alex: I miss the magic, Dad.

Kris: And I miss you.

They embrace. Rudolph shakes his sleigh bells.

Kris: Sounds like Rudolph is getting impatient.

Pix: I'll miss you, Kris.

Willy: So will I.

Alex: I almost forgot. I've finally found a place for Willy.

Sandy: An institution? Daddy, no!

Alex: It's more like a sheltered workshop.

Pix: Where?

Alex: The North Pole.

Willy: You mean I'm going to live with Santa and be an elf?

Kris: Seems like a fine idea to me. Are you any good at sanding blocks?

Willy: That's my specialty.

The sleigh bells again.

Kris: Well, Willy. I guess we should be going.

Willy and Sandy embrace. Willy and Kris are about to leave.

Alex: Dad . . . I'm going to hold a referendum on the Christmas issue.

Pix: Really?

Alex: It's too late for this year, but with some work, we may have Christmas back by next year.

Sandy/Willy: Yay!

Pix: Well, we're going to have a Christmas celebration this year. Kris, how would you and Willy and Rudolph like to come to our place for Christmas dinner.

Kris: We'd be thrilled, Pix.

Willy: Can I invite my mother?

Alex: If she can spare the time from her pro-Christmas campaign.

Pix: Pro-Christmas?

Alex: She's responsible for Willy and he's the one who re-introduced Christmas to Split Hoof. Rather than face a charge of by-law infringement, she's started up a campaign to change the by-law.

Willy: Soon Split Hoof will have Christmas again.

Sandy: WE have Christmas NOW. *Hugs Alex.*

The Song of the Star *(Reprise)*
Alex:
Light was streaming down
Upon a scene of joy.
In a humble town
They found Him.

Kris and Pix join:
In a lowly stall
There slept a tiny Boy
But radiance was all
Around Him.

Sandy, Willy and Rudolph join:
They all knelt down before Him,
Both poor man and great King,

With love and glory for Him
They did sing
A song of joy, hope, love
For mankind.

Epilogue

The elves all break character and there is much excitement as they discuss the story.

Mylar: Aw, you guys, that was the best story ever!

There is the sound of jingle bells and the pole starts to flash on and off. They all freeze.

Baubles: It's the hot line!

All: SANTA CLAUS!

There is a mad scramble as they all try to answer it at once. Lectro appears embarrassed at his outfit. Suddenly, they all look to Mylar.

Willy: Why don't you get it?

Everyone encourages her. She picks up the phone.

Mylar: Hello. North Pole Workshop, Mylar speaking . . . Oh yes . . . Yes sir, I am the new elf here . . . Thank you. I'm very glad to be here . . . What's that? More orders? Sure. Shoot . . . 150 rag dolls. *Marzipan runs offstage.* Ten dozen Christmas-tree ornaments. *Baubles follows her.* Forty-eight video games. *Lectro also runs off.* One hundred building blocks. *Willy looks stunned.* And wrap each item individually? *Sparkle disappears.* No problem. December 24th is our deadline . . . For me? For Christmas? *Thinks.* Yeah. How about a permanent job? . . . Well, thank you very much! Yeah, see you soon . . . Oh, that's very funny, Santa. Bye.

Indicates to Willy that Santa is Ho-Ho-Ho-ing at the other end of the line. She joins Willy.

You're right, Willy. There ought to be Christmas.

Willy: Welcome to the family.

The music begins for the finale which is an echo-chorus rendition of "The Song of the Star"—Reprise.

As the finale ends, there are company bows, Baubles organizes the dismantling of the pole and the elves all leave the stage.

■

Dr. Barnardo's Pioneers
Rick McNair

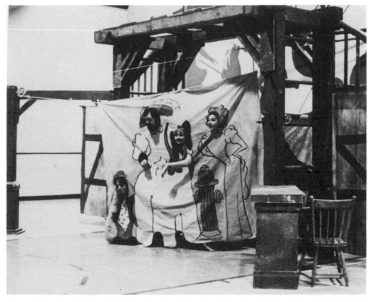

The man in the bowler hat, Mrs. Grundy, a Doggie, and a Thin Lady
discuss their opinions of the Barnardo orphans.

Dr. Barnardo's Pioneers was originally produced by Theatre Calgary's Stage-Coach Players in 1978 with the following cast:

Milton Branton
Vicki Hargreaves
Duval Lang
Grant Lowe
Sandy Mayzell

Directed by Rick McNair
Designed by Ron Fedoruk

For permission to produce this play and information about royalties please contact:

Shari Caldwell
First Artists Management
1255 Yonge Street, Suite 303
Toronto, Ontario
Canada   M4T 1W6

The setting of the play is in the back yard of a neat old home, not too far from downtown Calgary. It is 1981, a late spring day, just a little after lunch. The stage is empty and we hear:

Little Orphan Annie's come to our house to stay.
And wash the cups and saucers up, an' brush the crumbs away
And shoo the chickens off the porch, an' dust the hearth and sweep.
And make the fire, an' bake the bread, and earn her board and keep.

Sarah enters and crosses to basket. She is a determined woman. We would estimate her to be seventy at most, when in reality she is eighty. She is wearing a sweater over her dress. Sarah notices someone and starts to talk to this unseen person while she sorts out the laundry.

Sarah: So, you decided to come after all, did you? I still think you're wasting your time in coming home. I'm not as special as you say I am. I don't see how my story could be of any interest to you or anybody else for that matter. It's true I went to the Barnardo home over in England before I came to Canada, but lots of others did too. Now, look here, I am not going to be one of those old fools that talks about the good old days . . . people aren't interested in hearing how hard my life was. Everybody has got problems. You know, I heard some old people and some not quite so old people talk like *imitates some old busybody* "I remember back in 19-0-7 when the blizzards swept the prairies and I walked 2, no 4, or was it 8, no it was 10 miles in that blinding storm." Bores me to death anyway. Besides you wouldn't listen even if it was true. You'd yawn and go right back to your television sets . . . another thing. You called me a pioneer. Well, I washed clothes then, washed them all my life, still do. You don't see them putting pictures of people washing clothes on the cover of history books, now do you?

Thomas enters from the house. He appears to be the same age as Sarah. He is carrying a large folder. Thomas is wearing a wool cardigan over his shirt. Sarah does not see him.

Anyway, there are no fellows with white hats, no fellows with black hats, no Charlie's Angels, or Magnum P.I. So, what could I tell you anyway?

Thomas: You could tell them lots of things, Sarah. Things that would interest most of them.

Sarah: Now here's a talker for you. This is my brother, Thomas.

Thomas: How do you do?

Sarah: Now Thomas will gladly tell you anything . . . look at that folder he has, probably has pictures of himself in it.

Thomas: I hear you Sarah. You don't shame me. This folder has lots of bits from our lives.

Sarah: Oh Thomas, they're just pieces of paper.

Thomas: Pieces of us, if you know how to remember with them. You're just a pessimist there Sarah.

Sarah: Practical, Thomas, just practical.

Thomas: You are the doubting Thomas, not me. We are having a good life. I think it would make a good story.

Sarah: And Henry Winkler, The Fonz, would be you in the movie, I suppose.

Thomas: Maybe. *Chuckles and imitates The Fonz.*

Now, here is a picture of the ship we sailed over on Sarah, the *S. S. Corinthian.* I might mention here that our late PM, the Right Honorable Lester B. Pearson, sailed on her in W. W. I.

Sarah: I didn't know that.

Thomas: I don't know of many people now-a-days could do what we did: start a new land, start without parents, and . . .

Sarah: Wash a lot of clothes and wash a lot of floors.

Thomas: That too. Now this piece of paper tells about the first Barnardo boy. It's a copy of a newspaper article about a hundred years ago. It sort of tells about . . . *Looks through the paper.*

Sarah brings stool down stage for Thomas.

Sarah: You'd better get comfortable. He's started.

Thomas: It sort of tells about Jim Jarvis, a fellow that lived at Barnardo's house.

Jim Jarvis enters. He is dressed in rags as if he has just come from a London slum. He can not be seen by Tom and Sarah. Jim says his lines directly to the audience.

Jim: That's not quite right, I went to his school, where he taught at, and after he was done with teaching, I asked if I could kip there. That means sleep to you.

Thomas: Dr. Barnardo thought the whole thing absurd.

Jim: Absurd. *Absurd is said together.* Who would want to sleep in the schoolroom.

Thomas: Barnardo asked him, "What would your mother think?"

Jim: I ain't got no mother.

Thomas: Then Barnardo asked him about his father.

Jim: Ain't got no father.

Thomas: Barnardo looked down at Jim and said . . . "Stuff and nonsense boy. Don't tell me such stories. You say you haven't got a mother or father. Where are your friends? Where do you live?"

Jim: I didn't have any friends. I didn't live anywhere. The streets was me home. I lived with a bunch of boys down near Wopping Way. I did odd jobs with a boatman, to help on his barge. He treated me very bad. Knocked me about somethin' frightful. He used to beat me for nothing and sometimes I didn't have nothin' to eat for days. Sometimes, for fun, he'd set the dog on me and he chewed me up somethin' frightful. Finally I couldn't take it no more and I runned away. I thought I were going to be happy now, 'specially as most people took pity on me a give me a penny now and then. But lor, sir, the police were the worse; they always kept a-movin' me on. Twice I were up before the magistrate for sleepin' out. When the bobbies catched me, sometimes, they'd let me off with a kick or a good knock on the side of the 'ead. But one night an awful cross fellow caught me sleepin' on a doorstep an' locked me up. Then I got six days at the workhouse, an' afterwards runned away; an' ever since I've been in and out, up an' down, where I could. I ain't had no luck at all, an' it's been sleepin' out on an empty stomach almost every night.

Then Barnardo asked me if there were more boys like me in London.

Oh yes, sir, lots . . . 'eaps of 'em; more than I could count. So he asked me to take him to where some of them poor boys were and I told him,

That oi will, sir. I did too.

Jim exits.

Thomas: So, Jim led Dr. Barnardo through the alleys and slums of London and showed him a group of ragged boys sleeping out on a roof top with no covering of any kind to keep out the cold. Well, right then and there Dr. Barnardo decided he had to do something about these children and that's how the Homes got started. Course, that was a long time ago, about 1886, I think.

I read that *Oliver Twist* book and I figure that's what it was like for Jim back there. *To the unknown interviewer.* Now our story.

Sarah's and my story, starts about 50 years after poor old Jim's. We weren't the same as him though. We have parents, but they just couldn't feed us.

Sarah: One day our father took us all out, all six of us except Martha, the oldest. He put Mary, Bess and Faith into two different homes. Then he brought Thomas and me to the big building that said in big letters above our head **Dr. Barnardo's School**—"No destitute child ever refused admission".

Thomas: We didn't know what was going on.

Sarah: Neither did our Mother. When we left she just said good-bye. And that's the last we ever saw of her.

Thomas and Sarah exit. While they are backstage they are changing costumes into those of little kids. They continue talking while making the change. Their voices become younger with an English accent. The next few scenes take place in the Barnardo Home, a school type building.

Thomas: I was scared. When we saw the Matron, I thought she was putting us in jail. Remember, that's when we met Willy.

Sarah: I was eight years old.

Thomas: I must have been seven then.

Sarah: That Matron, she looked so big.

Enter Sarah and Thomas

Thomas: And mean . . .

Sarah: And ugly, with funny frizzy hair.

Matron enters stage left. She is ten feet tall. Matron is an actress sitting on the shoulders of an actor, with both of them covered in a long dress. The actor speaks and the actress moves her mouth.

Father: *Offstage voice.* Please just take my kids, I can't feed them.

Matron: Name.

Thomas: Where's my father.

Matron: Your name.

Thomas: Tommy.

Matron: All of it.

Thomas: Thomas Wright.

Matron: *Looking at Sarah.* Yours?

Sarah: Sarah Josephine Wright.

Matron: So, you want to be Barnardo children.

Thomas: I don't know.

Matron: Do you or don't you?

Sarah: What's a Barnardo child?

Matron: You live, go to school and work in Dr. Barnardo's School.

Sarah: *Thinking.* Go to school . . .

Matron: Yes.

Thomas: After school, we go home to kip?

Matron: You will eat, study, work and sleep here.

Sarah: Well, we might stay here, but only until Christmas.

Matron: I'm afraid that will not be your decision.

Thomas: Maybe we will and maybe we won't.

Matron: You can eat three times a day here.

Sarah: Three times?

Matron: You will like it here. *Sarah and Thomas start to leave.* You will like . . . Wait!

Matron exits muttering "You will like it here" etc.

Willie enters. He is the same age as Sarah and Thomas. He is extremely confident, to the point of being a know-it-all.

Willie: Just get here?

Thomas: A while ago.

Willie: I can tell.

Sarah: How?

Willie: You look like the roof is going to fall on your head.

Thomas: Is that so.

Willie: Yes.

Sarah: What's your name?

Willie: Willie. W. W. to you.

Thomas: W. W.?

Willie: They call me Will-he Won't-he, but I made them shorten it. What's your name?

Thomas: Tommy.

Sarah: Sarah.

Willie: Won't be for long. You can be Freckles and you can be . . .

Thomas: Ah, er . . .

Willie: Mumbles. That's it. Now you stick to me and you'll be alright.

Thomas: Thanks. Well, what do we do here?

Willie: We work and do all sorts of things. Some of those things we aren't supposed to do. *Trying to impress.*

Sarah: What sort of things?

Willie: I don't tell girls.

Tom: She's not a girl, she's my sister.

Willie: You just look at the list of do's and don't's in the hall . . . I've done all the don't's.

Tom: Really?

Willie: Well, Mumbly, you look like a lucky lad. I'll see if I can get you in the bread and butter brigade.

Tom: What's that?

Willie: Why, you butter the bread and eat all you can nick.

Tom: That's good?

Willie: Good, if you don't get caught.

Sarah: What happens if you get caught?

Willie: *Trying to scare them.* Well, you go in front of the boss and he puts you in the black hole for two or three days and all you get to eat is bread and water.

Tom: Really?

Willie: Really. You don't wet your bed, do you?

Sarah: We don't.

Willie: That's lucky for you, because if you did, you would have to show them your wet bed and then they take you to a room and shoot water out of the hose at you. Then you have to wash your sheets. You miss breakfast and everyone knows where you have been.

Tom: Really?

Willie: Really. And sometimes when you are really bad, they send you to Canada.

Tom: Oh. *Does not know what that means.* How did you get here?

Willie: Me mum asked if I would go to a place where I could eat three times a day. I said sure. So here I am. *To Sarah* Oh, by the way, she'll have to go.

Tom: No she won't. She's with me.

Willie: Don't matter. This place is only for boys. Girls go someplace else.

Sarah: No.

At this moment, the Matron and the Beadle appear. The children turn towards them. Tom and Sarah say a silent good-bye.

Willie: It's not so bad. You'll get used to it.

Beadle taps his cane four times while the Matron claps her hands, they start marching in place and the children march to separate places to indicate where their beds are. It should appear that Sarah is in a different place from the boys.

Matron: How to make a bed.

Matron and Beadle: Take a sheet, shake it out, place it on your bed,
Tuck it in, nice and tight, one end open for your head.
Then the blanket, it comes next, exactly on the sheet,
Tuck it in, nice and tight, especially 'round your feet.
Pillows . . . . . . on!

Matron exits. The children were miming how to make a bed and marching in place while making the bed. The Beadle comes over and inspects the boys' beds.

Beadle: *To Willie.* That's not how you make a bed. Do it again!

Beadle exits. Matron enters and gives Sarah a book. Sarah reads the book while the boys are talking.

Willie: Pssst. Hey Mumbles.

Tom: Yes?

Willie: You want to break a rule?

Tom: Well, uh, I don't know.

Willie: I got something for you. *Hands Tom a piece of bread.*

Tom: Where'd you get that?

Willie: *Laughing.* No eating in bed.

Beadle: *Offstage.* All quiet for evening prayer.

Beadle and Matron enter.

All: *Sing.* Jesus, tender shepherd, hear me
Bless Thy little lambs tonight.

They start exiting.

Through the darkness, be Thou near me
Keep me safe 'till morning light.
Amen.

Beadle: *Offstage.* William Collins and Thomas Wright, come here . . . Quickly now.

The boys enter on the double.

Beadle: You boys have been selected to go to Canada. Congratulations. Wait here, I have something for you. *Exits.*

Willie: Who told on us?

Thomas: I meant to ask you before. What's Canada?

Willie: It's a place in the north of England. Near Newcastle.

Thomas: Is it very big?

Willie: Not really.

Thomas: Will it take long to get there?

Willie: Not really, two to three days at the most.

Voices offstage: *Singing.* Oh, Canada. It's really cold out there.

Beadle: *Enters with laundry basket.* I have some things for you that you will need in Canada. We chose you boys because we think you will do just fine in Canada. Go ahead, try them on. *He exits.*

Voices offstage: *Singing.* Oh Canada, best take long underwear.

Thomas: What are these for? *Holding up long underwear.*

Willie: They're for wearing. Stupid.

Thomas: Front or back? *Looking at the flap in the underwear.*

Willie: Depends if it's winter or summer.

Voices Offstage: *Singing.* Where freezing winds and blowing snow go on well into June.

Thomas: Oh. *Puts hands in toque.* Is this right?

Willie: *Putting it over hands.* Yes. Your hands get cold there. It's near Scotland, you know?

Thomas: Then what are these for? *Holding up mittens.*

Willie: You use them when you are riding horses. See you've got to hold on to the reins.

Thomas: Oh. *Bends down. Willie jumps on his back. They exit with basket.*

Voices Offstage: *Singing.* Oh Canada. Your new, not native land. Oh, Canada. *Last Oh, Canada is spoken in despair.*

Sarah crosses in confusion, holding the same clothes as the boys, while last line is being sung.

Harmonica playing Rule Britannia. Children enter slowly. The scene has changed to on board the Corinthian.

Beadle: You people are a select group and you should be proud of yourselves. You are going to a new land, a new life. It will not be easy. We at the Home will be helping all we can, we'll give help both moral, and practical . . . but in the end, your new life will depend on you.

Money should not be your measure of success. Remember your teachers, remember that it is harder for a rich man to enter heaven than it is for a camel to pass through the eye of a needle. Work hard and you will be rewarded. You will build for yourself, and for your new land . . . Canada! We know you have the strength, the fibre. Not everyone is able to do what we are asking you to do. Spread the Barnardo Homes' mission to this new land.

Good luck. God speed.

Beadle takes Barnardo poles and sign off. Bosun's whistle. Backstage voices—Blow the man down . . . da da da. Ship's bell—4 bells. The actors give a movement to show they are at sea. Sarah is on a different part of the ship.

Thomas: Ten days! This is taking a lot longer than you said it would.

Willie: That's because this old *Corinthian* is going so slow.

Thomas: I don't feel so good.

Willie: Hey. One of the sailors told me this great cure for seasickness.

Thomas: Really, what's that?

Willie: Well, you get a piece of salt pork and you tie a string around it . . . Then you swallow the pork and pull it back up by the string.

Thomas heaves. Sound of foghorn.

Willie: *Pulling string from mouth.* Seemed like a good idea to me. *He heaves. Sound of foghorn.*

Sarah: When I get to Canada, I'm not staying with any family. As soon as I get off that boat I'm going to run away and live in the forest. And I'll take my book with me and then when I decide, I'll go to school and study how to be a schoolteacher and I'll be the best schoolteacher in England, Canada, or any of those places. Good morning class. My name is Miss Wright.

Omnes: *Offstage.* Good morning, Miss Wright.

Thomas: When I get to Canada, there's going to be a really nice family waiting for me there and I'm going to be a farmer. I'll have a mother and a dad . . . and dad and I will do farm stuff together . . . and we'll all be real happy . . . when I get to Canada.

Willie: I won't need a family in Canada. I'm going to go to the wilds and live with the Indians. They're going to teach me to hunt and to trap and I'm going to be a rich fur trader.

Thomas: *Makes a raspberry.*

Willie: Well, I am. Do you know how they get the fur off the animals after they kill them?

Thomas: No.

Willie: Well, I do. You get this big knife, see, and you cut the carcass right down the middle and then you open it up and reach your hand in and pull out all the guts.

Thomas turns away heaving. Sound of foghorn.

Willie: Then I'm going to go to the Yukon to find GOLD!

Bosun whistle.

Voice Offstage: Land Ho!

They see land then hubbub—all speak at once. There is a great deal of rushing about, at the conclusion of which four people take up a painted banner with Mrs. Grundy, Man in Bowler, Doggie, and Thin Lady painted on it. There are holes cut out for the actors' faces. The banner is painted in cartoon style. Men play women and vice versa. If doing the five character version, the actor playing Thomas is not included.

Mrs. Grundy: Did you know they are still sending those Barnardo orphans over here?

Man in Bowler: Is that so, Mrs. Grundy?

Doggie: Bark!

Mrs. Grundy: They have sent thousands since they started.

Thin Lady: My, my.

Mrs. Grundy: And you know what kind of children they are.

Man and Lady: Yes, we do, Mrs. Grundy.

Doggie: Bark, bark.

Mrs. Grundy: They are street urchins, pick pockets and they are, dare I say it, without parents they can name.

Man and Lady: Tsk, tsk, tsk.

Doggie: Bark, bark, bark.

Mrs. Grundy: Our government is just too generous.

Man: Right you are, Mrs. Grundy.

Mrs. Grundy: Canada should be for the Canadians!

Lady: Three cheers for us. Hip, Hip . . .

Omnes: Hooray!

Doggie: Bark!

Lady: Hip, Hip . . .

Omnes: Hooray!

Doggie: Bark!

Lady: Hip, Hip . . .

Omnes: Hooray!

Doggie: Bark!

All: *Exit singing.* Oh, Canada. We stand on guard for thee.

Thomas and Willie enter. They are waiting at a railway station. There is the whistle of a departing train.

Mr. Campbell enters. He is a farmer in his late twenties.

Campbell: Are you Thomas Wright? *Willie had thought that Campbell had come for him.*

Willie: He is.

Thomas: Yes Sir, Thomas Wright.

Campbell: So, you're the boy from Barnardo's eh?

Thomas: Yes Sir.

Campbell: So, you're going to be a farmer, Thomas.

Thomas: Yes, Sir.

Campbell: Where's your gear?

Thomas: This is it, Sir.

Campbell: That's all you've got?

Thomas: No, I have a trunk coming sometime. This is what they gave us for Canada.

Campbell: You can use that and a lot more. Do you know much about farming?

Thomas: Well . . . not that much, Sir, but I can learn quickly.

Campbell: Good for you. Don't want the Indians to get you.

Thomas: Are there Mounties nearby?

Campbell: Don't you worry . . .

Thomas: Chickens . . .

Campbell: What?

Thomas: Chickens . . . I know how to take care of chickens.

Campbell: Oh, that's good, that's good, but we have cows.

Thomas: Oh. *Sadly.*

Campbell: What else can you do?

Thomas: I can cut wood.

Campbell: Oh that'll be just fine, just fine. So, welcome Thomas. Welcome to Canada, Ontario, Muskoka, and Campbell's farm.

Thomas: That's a lot of places, Sir.

Campbell: All of them is right here. Come on, Son. Let's go home. *Picks up suitcase and exits. Train whistle.*

Willie: *Enters.* My new family will be so glad to see me. They are so lucky I am here. You know, I can really help you. Things will be better for you now that I am here. Willie here, never fear. Where's my room? What's for supper? . . . Maybe they don't want me. Why should they? I really don't know how to do anything. They will send me back . . . No, they won't, I'm too valuable. I'm strong. I learn quick. I'm English. I am a natural leader. They need me . . . They might say I am not that big. I don't look too strong. Maybe they don't like English kids. Maybe they want someone else . . . they might send me back . . . Send me back . . . never . . . I can give too much . . . I can show them a lot. I will drive horses. Probably have my own horse. I'll call him Galahad . . . I'll go back to the home. You can keep your farm for all I care.

Voice Offstage: Willie, Willie Collins? Over here.

Willie: Yes, Sir. *Willie exits on the run.*

Offstage voices humming "There's No Place Like Home." Singing "This is the way we make the bread . . ." Nora enters. She is a young, very English newlywed. She is trying to make bread.

Nora: That should be enough . . . Ah . . . Is it too much? Not enough? . . . I will never be able to make bread. It should be so simple. *She goes to the table and reads letter she has been writing to her mother.*

August 11th, 1911.

Dear Mother,

It is beautiful here. Things are certainly different than they are in England. Even the song birds sing different music. *Looks at her cooking.* I am still having some small problems *laughs* with my cooking. I have found there are disadvantages in having a maid back in England. Having her do everything did not prepare me for a life in Canada. John and I will be getting a girl from Barnardo's to help around the house. She will be such a help with the cooking. She will also tell me what is going on in London.

We have thirty-five acres ready and will soon have the land signed over to us. Does Father still laugh when he tells people we live near WaWa?

Pause. A knock is heard. Nora answers the door. Stage manager knocks on wood backstage while Sarah mimes it out front.

Nora: Just a minute. *She tidies quickly, then goes to the door. Mimes opening it.*

Nora: Who are you?

Sarah: I'm Sarah Wright.

Nora: You're not the young woman from Barnardo's?

Sarah: Yes Ma'am.

Nora: Aren't you a bit young?

Sarah: I'm ten and a half years old.

Nora: I don't . . . just thought . . . never mind . . . come on in.

Sarah: I will for now, but I don't know if I'm staying.

Nora: Oh?

Long pause.

Sarah: I'm going to be a teacher.

Nora: Oh, that's nice.

Sarah: Is the school near here?

Nora: Not that far. It's about four miles. You will be able to go sometimes.

Sarah: I have to go.

Nora: There are lots of things to do here. Cooking, washing, firewood, helping John with some chores, garden work, making preserves . . .

Sarah: I don't know anything about that kind of thing.

Nora: Oh.

Sarah: When do I do those things? Do I have a schedule?

Nora: That's a good idea. Let's make a schedule. On Monday, we will bake, Tuesday, we will wash, on Wednesday, you can help John, Thursday you can . . .

Sarah: If I do all those things when do I go to school?

Nora: There is so much to do here. I can read and write. I will teach you and some days you can get to school.

Pause. Nora takes Sarah's suitcases, puts them offstage.

Sarah: Do you have any books?

Nora: Yes, a few. I have *Wuthering Heights* by Emily Bronte. I love that story! *Looks for response.* We have . . . The Bible, of course! . . . And I have my Homemaker's Guide. It has lots of

interesting things . . . and the Eaton's catalogue comes every
spring! *Changing the subject.* What did you bring from London?
What are the people wearing in England now? What news did you
bring?

Sarah: I didn't get out from the home much . . . *Pause. The silence
becomes uncomfortable. Indicating mixture in bowl.* Is there
something I can do with this?

Nora: Can you make bread?

Sarah: They showed us some of it at the home . . .

Sarah takes off her coat. Indicating rolling pin. You don't use that
for making bread, do you?

Nora: No.

Sarah: Well, I could take this . . . and . . .

Nora: And dump it out?

Sarah: And start over.

Nora: I'll show you where the kitchen is. *They both exit.*

At the Campbell's farm. Thomas and Mr. Campbell enter.

Campbell: Come, Tom, let's get some of this wood cut.

Thomas: Right away, Mr. Campbell.

Campbell: We will need lots for winter. *Hands Tom the end of the
two-handed saw.*

Thomas: We still have some time.

Campbell: You're getting on well here.

Thomas: It's good here.

Campbell: Not the same as where you are from, eh?

Thomas: Lots different.

Campbell: Would you like to stay here?

Thomas: I guess so . . . sure.

Campbell: I mean to live . . . would you like me and Anne to be
your . . . well, uh . . . We want to adopt you. Would you like that?

Thomas: Really, Mr. Campbell, I sure would. Yes.

Campbell: Good. I'll write to the Barnardo home for permission.
Let's go and find Anne. *They exit together.*

Train whistle.

Willie: *Enters.* With the next family, I'm going to try something
different. I'll try polite. Hello Sir. I am pleased to be here. I am sure
I will be able to be of service to you. Your experience will be a great

benefit to me. You look like a very kind man . . . That sounds weak. Farmers want strong, not weak. Hi. My name's Willie. What needs to be done? We'd better get to it right away. I'll get my things. Where is the wagon? No, that won't impress . . . Maybe . . .

Voice Offstage: William? William Collins?

Willie: *Exits with fingers crossed behind his back.* Yes sir.

Harmonica playing "Silent Night", couple of bars. Nora and Sarah enter.

Nora: It's too bad there is so much snow.

Sarah: *Looking out the window.* I'm going to miss being in the school Christmas concert.

Nora: I know. We could pretend this is the school and we will have it here.

Sarah: It's silly to do that kind of thing.

Nora: It's not silly if you want to do it. Besides it is acting.

Sarah: There's no one here to watch.

Nora: Yes there is. John and I. We have seen real plays in London so we know what an audience is supposed to do. Let's see. You stand there. No, I will introduce you first. *Goes to area they are using for stage.* Now. Miss Sarah Wright will recite the poem "Little Orphan Annie" by James Whitcomb Riley. Now enunciate clearly "Little Orphan Annie" by James Whitcomb Riley. *Sarah goes to centre and recites.*

Sarah: Little Orphan Annie by James Whitcomb Riley. *She does so in a very stiff manner.*
Little Orphan Annie's come to our house to stay.
And wash the cups and saucers up, and brush the crumbs away.
And shoo the chickens off the porch, and dust the hearth and sweep,
And make the fire and . . .

Nora: *Interrupting.* Did you choose the poem by yourself, Sarah?

Sarah: Yes I did, Mrs. MacLeod.

Nora: Fine, Sarah. Continue. No, start over again, only this time act out what you are saying . . .

Moves to face Sarah.

Little *gestures* Orphan Annie, Brush *gestures* the crumbs . . . Let us see what you are saying. Start.

Nora coaches Sarah through the recital. First one has an idea and then the other.

Sarah: Little Orphan Annie's come to our house to stay. And wash the cups and saucers up, and brush the crumbs away. And shoo the chickens off the porch, *big kicking gesture* and dust the hearth and sweep. And make the fire, and bake the bread, and earn her board and keep. And all the other children, when the supper things are done, they sit around the kitchen fire and have the most of fun listening to the witch tales that Annie tells about. And the gobble-uns will get you if you don't watch out!

Nora: Bravo, bravo. *Applause.* Merry Christmas, Sarah.

Hum or harmonica "Oh Come All Ye Faithful" offstage.

Sarah: Merry Christmas, Mrs. MacLeod.

Pause.

Nora: I know, let's go get something for a costume. We have got to get your theatrical debut correct.

"Deck the Halls With Boughs of Holly" is played on harmonica or accordian offstage.

At the Campbell farm. Thomas and Mr. Campbell are busy cutting wood as the man from the home enters.

Johnson: Good day, Mrs. Campbell. Tom. I'm Mr. Johnson from the Barnardo Home.

Campbell: How do you do?

Thomas: Hello, sir.

Johnson: I've got a letter for you, Tom. And since I was passing this way on some other business, I brought it along. It's a letter from your sister.

Thomas: A letter from Sarah.

Johnson: Yes, since I was coming anyway.

Campbell: About the adoption?

Johnson: That's what I am here for. I must say I concurred one hundred percent with your request to adopt Tom . . . I think that you and Mrs. Campbell would make excellent parents and I said so when I forwarded the application to our head office in Stepney Causeway.

Campbell: But?

Johnson: Yes, but since Tom's mother is still living we had to get her approval . . . and quite frankly, she said no . . . here's the letter . . . she said Tom could not be adopted while she is still alive.

Thomas: But I want to live here.

Johnson: Yes, I can see that.

Campbell: He can stay here, can't he?

Johnson: Actually, . . . well . . . the policy of the Home does not encourage this.

Campbell: So?

Johnson: It is not my decision, but it is thought better for all concerned if we take Tom away from here . . .

Thomas: No.

Johnson: Since it will be hard on all of us, I will call for Tom in the morning . . . at 9 o'clock. This was not my plan. . . Goodbye for now . . . It sure is a nice farm, Mr. Campbell.

Campbell: Goodbye. *Johnson exits. Tom and Campbell start to saw.* You go on up to the house, Tom. I'll finish by myself. Go on.

Tom exits. Campbell finishes cutting and exits. Train whistle.

At a railway station.

Nora: Do you have everything Sarah?

Sarah: Yes, I think so. Winnipeg will be nice.

Nora: Yes, I'm sure it will be. You know we don't want you to go. It's just that . . .

Sarah: I know, you don't have to . . .

Nora: We just could not pay the Barnardo Home $1 a day for you.

Sarah: That's a lot of money. I'm 13, old enough to support myself.

Train whistle.

Nora: Now don't lift things that are too heavy.

Sarah: Remember how much flour to put in the bread.

Nora: Now you should not stop your reading.

Sarah: And don't be fooled by what the Eaton's catalogue says.

Nora: Now you see that you eat enough. You are a young lady now.

Sarah: Don't burn your hand on the stove. *Train whistle, train sounds.* I will see more of the country since coming to Canada.

Nora: I've never been out of Ontario. You are fortunate.

Sarah: Nora, I'm glad I stayed. You taught me a lot of things.

Nora: You taught me more. *Train steam.* Here, this is for you.

Sarah: *Wuthering Heights.* This is your favorite book. You shouldn't have.

Nora: I should have.

Embrace.

Sarah: I'd better get going now before we both get silly.

Voice: All aboard. *Train starts up. Whistle.*

Willie enters with all sorts of horse harnesses.

Willie: Alright horse, you are going to be harnessed. *Horse laugh.* Well, don't worry, before I put this on you I'll try it on myself. *Takes blinders.* Let's see. *Puts it on as pants.* This part must be for the rider. *Gets more and more involved with the harness. In fact all tangled up.* Maybe I haven't got it quite right. *Horse laugh.* I wish I hadn't told him I know everything about horses . . . I know . . . Sir, what I meant is that I know everything about English horses. This one is a Canadian horse. *Horse laughs. Willie exits.* Who asked you?

Thomas is sitting on the station platform.

Talbot: What's your name?

Thomas: Tom . . . Tom Wright.

Talbot: Yeah. You're the one then. My name is Tom. Can't have two Toms on the same farm. What's your middle name?

Thomas: I don't have a middle name, sir.

Talbot: Well, your new name can be John, Yeah, John.

Thomas: John?

Talbot: You get in the wagon over there, John, while I go to the store. I'll be back in a few minutes. *Exits.*

Thomas: *Loudly.* Tom. *Softly.* John. *Exits.*

"No Place Like Home" should be played softly under the end of this scene and the first part of the next scene.

Brass knocker sound backstage while Sarah mimes knocking.

Knock at door. Mrs. Jordan goes to answer.

Mrs. Jordan: Good day. You are the Barnardo girl. Sarah Wright. I'm Mrs. Jordan. Come in.

Sarah: Yes ma'am. I'll just close . . .

Mrs. Jordan: I trust you had a good trip? I think you'll like Winnipeg.

Sarah: Yes. I did, thank you.

Mrs. Jordan: Here is a list of the things you will be required to do. In addition, you will note that breakfast is promptly at 8, lunch at 12, tea at 4 in the parlour and dinner at 8. Also, you will be given the usual half day off every two weeks and I am sure you will find your quarters suitable.

Sarah: This letter is for you.

Mrs. Jordan: Thank you. *Reads letter.* Well, I foresee no difficulties as I have agreed to pay the Barnardo Home $1 a day for your services. I will show you to your room. Follow me. Quickly, this way. *Both exit.*

Same music as between previous scenes.

Willie enters. Jews harp preceeds Willie throwing his bedroll on.

Willie: I hate horses. I hate farming. Gotta get out of here. Can still be a trapper. Goin' to the Klondike. Maybe I'll find gold. Yes, gold. *Exits.*

Jews harp.

Talbot enters with pitchfork, puts it down.

Tom runs in.

Talbot: Did you get the work done?

Thomas: No, Mr. Talbot. The cattle broke through the fence again and got into Anderson's pasture, so I couldn't get the pigsty and chicken coop musked out 'cause I had to fix the fence and . . .

Talbot: Did you get the work done?

Thomas: The cattle broke . . . no.

Talbot: You haven't had a lickin' in a long time. Get the whip. Move!

Thomas gets whip and hands it to Talbot.

Talbot: Kneel down. Kneel down!

Thomas: No.

Talbot: I said kneel down.

Thomas: No, please Mr. Talbot. No more please.

Talbot: I'll teach you . . . *Talbot advances on Tom. Tom grabs pitchfork.*

Thomas: You touch me once more with that whip and I'll run this right through your belly. I mean it.

Talbot: Better finish your work. *Exit.*

Thomas runs off.

Sarah enters. Starts to polish mirror down centre. Pulls out a list.

Sarah: Mrs. Jordan, I want to ask you some questions please. I've written things down so I won't forget them. One. Paul and I want to get married. We are going to move to Alberta. I am going to become a teacher there. Two. Would you write to the Barnardo Home to get official approval. Three. *Mrs. Jordan crosses.*

Mrs. Jordan: Sarah, have you got the tea service polished?

Sarah: *Hiding the list.* Yes, Mrs. Jordan. *Takes out list again. Mrs. Jordan exits.* Three. I'm sure you'll have no problem getting the home to send someone else out, and four, will you come to my wedding?

Mrs. Jordan crosses back.

Sarah: Mrs. Jordan, may I speak to you for a minute please?

Mrs. Jordan: I'm quite busy Sarah. Is it important?

Sarah: Yes, but I have written things down so I won't forget them.

Mrs. Jordan: Fine then, but please be quick.

Sarah: One. Paul and I want to get married. You remember Paul?

Mrs. Jordan: Certainly. Fine boy.

Sarah: We are going to Alberta and I want to teach there. Would you write the Barnardo Home to get official approval?

Mrs. Jordan: Certainly.

Sarah: I'm sure you'll have no problem getting the home *Mrs. Jordan exits* to send someone else out . . . *Looks up and sees she is alone.* And will you come to my wedding? *Sarah looks at herself in the mirror, feels alone, then she imagines her life as she will make it.*

Song from backstage—"Monday Morning".

Thomas enters quietly. Watches Sarah. When Sarah notices Thomas she is brought back to the present. Glances in mirror as old Sarah, chuckles and dresses slowly while Thomas is speaking.

Thomas: I ran away from Talbot, but where could I run to? I went back to the Home, told them my story and when they found out I was telling the truth they sent me to a new place. I remember one day the farmer, a nice fellow, came to me and said . . .

Offstage Voice: We are finishing the threshing, Tom, and I won't be needing you tomorrow. The Barnardo Home says you have no more obligation to them, so I guess you're on your own.

Thomas: I had just turned sixteen, I had no money, no place to go and I didn't know what to do. The farmer gave me a few dollars of his own and I headed for Calgary. He thought I would be glad to go, but you're only glad to leave one place when you know you've got some other place to go to. It's funny but I had the same feeling about being on my own as I did when I went into the Barnardo Home for the first time. I was scared.

Sarah starts weeping.

Sarah: Well you can get lonely when you're all alone.

Thomas: It's not just that Sarah, it was hard for us.

Sarah: We did what we had to do Thomas; we all did.

Thomas: You know, I often wonder whatever happened to old Willie. I wonder where he is now.

Sarah: He could be rich, or a politician, or in jail.

Thomas: Maybe. Well I think we can be proud of ourselves. Sarah, we did real well. I can remember having to eat pig slop at Talbot's farm, I was so hungry. By the way Sarah, what are we having for supper tonight? Seriously, I remember working every day and not getting paid a dime. But I did real well. I made it. Well, we both did.

Sarah: I never became a schoolteacher, in those days married women couldn't be schoolteachers. But I'm not ashamed of it. Paul and I, God rest his soul, had a good life and when we came out to Alberta I found my brother Thomas.

Thomas: Not many people nowadays could do what we did, Sarah. We were special.

Sarah: Now Thomas, I've got a granddaughter, she talks a little different, acts different, and certainly dresses different, but she still wants and hopes for the same things I did. I'm sure she could come through if she had to . . .

Thomas: Well, I'm not so sure Sarah. There were lots of other things we did too, you know. Remember the time I was in Turner Valley and . . .

Sarah: Now Thomas you're not going to tell them that story . . .

Thomas: We started up the oilfield.

Sarah: Thomas, we can't tell them everything. Let's go inside and have a nice cup of tea. We're doing just fine. *Exiting.*

. . . Thank you.

■

The Day Jake Made Her Rain
W.O. Mitchell

*Trudy Cowan, **the Kid**, and Eliah Zarou, **Jake**, in the 1976
Alberta Theatre Projects production.*

photograph: Neil F. Macmillan

The Day Jake Made Her Rain had its first professional theatre performance at Alberta Theatre Projects in Calgary, Alberta on January 26, 1976 with the following cast:

Ma————————————————— Karen Austin
Kid ————————————————— Trudy Cowan
Jake ———————————————— Stanley Coles/Elias Zarou
Old Man Gatenby ——————— Elias Zarou/Russell Scott

Directed by Douglas Riske
Designed by Grant Guy

Scene 1

The back yard of a southern Saskatchewan farmhouse. Along back stage and down left the brilliant blue of July prairie sky with the low far line of prairie horizon. On this to the right might be indicated perhaps a distant privy with slant roof—a moon cut-out. Because of the general nature of the play, the set could be given a stylized, slightly exaggerated execution, fences inordinately drunken, flowers melodramatically wilting. Up right and extending down left stands the back porch used during the summer months as a summer kitchen. It consists simply of a shallow shed roof supported on posts so that the prairie-sky blue of the back drop is seen right through. Shingles are curling; paint is scaling; eaves troughing sags, one length of this hanging down across one corner at just the height to catch a man's head as he takes the short cut through the side and to the gate which is in the fence down from the downstage edge of the porch. A screen door opens to the house; a table stands just above the door and against the house wall. In the left corner of the porch upstage is a stand roughly built of two-by-fours, holding a wash basin, on the porch beside it a water pail, a slop pail. A long towel hangs from a nail on a post.

An unpainted and uncertain fence extends from the porch down the right side of the stage to the front where it turns and runs perhaps two feet across between audience and players. This may cut down stage frontage but the fence is not solid and there must be a piece running in this way for a man or a child to sit on. Just down from the corner up left, a pump with handle canting high, and just below centre left a shed indicated with door opening to the right. Here are tools of various sorts, a kindling box, coal.

It is understood that the yard extends out into the audience. During the climax of the play it is to be assumed that the people are Crocus District folks who have come to see Jake make her rain. During that portion of the play actors with a comment or a line or two will be out front to give them from there. If it can be managed and handled without anarchy raising its ugly head, a chicken (white wine-dot) should be permitted the run of the stage.

At rise—the porch, yard, shed are seen in brilliant noon light, the sky that seems to swallow them, quite cloudless. Jake Trumper is seated on the piece of fence downstage, shoulders slumped. He is a long, lean hired man in his late sixties with a stained and battered hat pushed to the back of his head. Old Man Gatenby, sitting on the porch steps at the downstage corner, is in the act of squeezing off the corner of a plug of chewing tobacco. He is a rather florid faced, beefier version of Jake and is also wearing denim overalls. Both are uninterestedly watching the Kid, whose rear is slowly coming out of the shed door. He turns with arms full of kindling to go to the door to open with his toe, then walks across stage to the porch. As he comes to the steps and Mr. Gatenby . . .

Kid: Excuse me, Mr. Gatenby.

Gate: Hmmmh. *As Kid gets to door and without turning his head.* Kin tell her I ain't stayin' to dinner.

Jake: Wasn't asked, was yah? *Waits for comment from Gate.* Kid's Ma—she figgers pleasant conversation aids the digestion.

Gate: That's nice.

Jake: Way you bin on the fight all mornin' . . .

Gate: I ain't bin on any fight.

Jake: Can't bring up anythin' without you startin' argument. We get to talkin' about rain an' rainmakers an' . . .

Gate: Ain' any such thing as rainmakers—a lotta . . .

Jake: Now Gate. *Swinging slowly down off the fence.* This country's had real rainmakers.

Gate: No she ain't.

Jake: Why—sure—you take Hatfield. *Crosses gate and goes to washstand and water pail, picks up dipper.* He made her rain way back . . .

Gate: You take him. Gives me the heartburn.

Jake: *As he dips dipper into pail.* He brung rain to Medicine Hat. Then there was this other fellah . . . *Lifts dipper high and turns it upside down—dry . . .* this other fellah comes right through Crocus District. *Bends down and picks up pail.* Brought all his rainmakin' machinery with him—set up on a CPR flatcar. He . . .

Gate: Just a sprinkly little shower. Didn't even lay the dust.

Jake: *Over his shoulder as he walks with pail towards the pump.* He contracked to git paid for anything he brought over an' above the av'rage rainfall.

Gate: *Has got up from porch step and is following Jake to the pump.* Didn't do so good out Yallah Grass way—ner at Broomhead—ner at Broken Shell—ner Union Jack . . .

Jake: *Who has hung pail on pump and started pumping.* Well, I ain't familiar with how he done at those places . . .

Gate: I'm telling you—he didn't do no—why they run him clear outa Broomhead.

Jake: *Still working with pump handle.* That didn't have a thing to do with him raining.

Gate: Why—it most certainly did!

Jake: *Letting go pump handle.* Dry. She's plumb dry!

Gate: Damn right she is an' no rainmaker's gonna—

Jake: Pump. Well's gone dry.

Ma: *From the house.* Jake—I'm waiting for that water!

Jake: Well's gone dry! She'll wait aitch of a long time before she gits water. *Turning on Gate.* They run him outa Broomhead all right but it was on accounta the extra ace hearts in the poker game over the Sanitary Cafe.

Gate: Was not.

Jake: She was.

Ma: *Who has come out on the porch.* Jake, I thought you were getting me water.

Jake: *To Gate.* She was. *To Ma.* Well's dry.

Ma: Dry!

Gate: Well, I say she was not. She was because he couldn't rain worth a whoop an' that was why they run him out of . . .

Ma: *A little impatient.* Are you two still arguing about rainmaking . . .

Jake: There was a big pot. They was playing a hand of Seven Toed Pete . . .

Ma: All right now—it's bad enough with everything dried up and having to go over to Tinchers for water now the well's . . . gone dry without you two . . .

Gate: *Who has stumped across to his place on the porch.* No rainmaker never made no rain machine—nor never brought—no rain— *Bites.* —to nobody. *Spits.*

Jake: Don't do that!

Gate: Huh? What?

Jake: Don't spit like that. So liberal.

Gate: Why not.

Jake: Sinful.

Gate: Sinful!

Jake: Why we're bakin' in this drought . . . Wastin' yer moisture that way.

Gate: Aaaahhh!

Ma: Water or no water—dinner in half an hour. Jake—I guess you'll have to hitch up and go over to Tinchers for . . .

Jake: *Taking up old position on the fence.* Yeah, yeah . . .

Ma: . . . water. *She turns away to the house.*

Gate: Trouble with you—you're superstitious.

Ma: Eat on the porch—stove's got that kitchen like a furnace. *As she meets Kid.* Son, set the dishes out for me. *Goes in house followed by Kid.*

Jake: Tinchers' went dry Tuesday. *Pause.* I ain't.

Gate: *Who has lost the train of conversation.* Ain't what?

Jake: Superstitious.

Gate: Oh. You believe in rainmakin' then you . . .

Jake: If they got the right kind of machine they can do it.

Gate: They can do it in a pig's ear.

Jake: Hell of an awkward place to raise wheat in.

Gate: *Gets up and goes to Jake.* It is impossible to rain with a machine. They can't do it.

Jake: They can so.

Gate: They can not.

Jake: They can so.

Gate: They can not.

Jake: They can so.

Kid enters with arms full of dishes which he proceeds to lay out on the table.

Jake: I seen it done.

Gate: You ain't.

Jake: I done it myself.

Kid, in the act of setting out a plate, looks up startled at this reaction from Jake.

Gate: You sure did not— *Pause as he realizes what Jake has just said.* You what?

Jake: *Long awkward pause.* Why . . . I . . . uh certain'y . . . certain'y I did . . . it . . . it was afore I . . . uh . . . afore I come to Crocus Districk.

Gate: *Who has risen and is advancing slowly and relentlessly on Jake.* You bet it was afore you come to Crocus Districk.

Kid has slowly come across the porch and down steps to stand before Jake.

Gate: Before you ever worked as hired man for anybody in this districk. I bin here just as long as you . . . and you ain't done no rainin' since I bin here. *Long pause.* Just—where—did—you—do any—rainin'?

Kid: Yeah, Jake—where did you . . .

Jake: Ought four. Manyberries way.

Gate: Is that so? Is—that—so!

Jake: Yep. *Rises from step and starts towards washstand.* They used to call me—uh—Sheet Lightnin' Trumper.

Gate: Did they now? Is—that—so?

Jake: Yep. *Begins business of washing his hands.*

Gate: *Oily.* Did—uh—you have much success out of this here rainmakin'?

Kid: Gee, Jake—did you?

Jake: In a way I did. Then— *Making motions of sloshing water over his face.* Then in a way I didn't.

Ma enters with bowls, vegetables, etc. and goes to place them on the table.

Gate: Either you brung her down er else you didn't bring her down.

Jake: *Turning with eyes squeezed shut and groping for towel.* I brung her down all right. Trouble was I didn't have no—uh— where the aitch is that towel . . .

Kid: *Jumping up to hand him the end of the towel.* Here, Jake . . .

Jake: *Daubs at face while others wait, including Ma who is now interested in Jake's rainmaking abilities.* No control. Lots of power but no control. *Finished, gives a snap to towel.* None of your light little misty rains—them skimpy quick little summer showers—when I rained I really rained. *Snaps towel for effect again—Kid jumps.* Both hands.

Gate: Uh-huh.

Jake: *Walking to the edge of porch front with basin.* Take Dominion Day in Ought Five . . .

Gate: *Leading him on.* Why, sure . . .

Jake: Got her turned on an' couldn't get her turned off all through August an' September. *Throws contents of basin on flowers that run along downstage edge of porch.* Hardly nobody got thrashed at all so she had to stand in the stook right through till Spring—then they didn't git no crop.

Gate: Why not?

Jake: *Casual as he sets back basin.* Mice.

Ma: Mïce!

Kid: Mice!

Gate: What did you say?

Jake: Mice. *Of course.*

Gate: *Pause.* Oh.

Ma: Oh.

Kid: Oh.

Jake: Stooks was fulla mice. Go by a field an' see alla them spikers an' field pitchers workin' without no pants . . .

Ma: No pants!

Gate: *Incoherent.* What did you say?

Jake: WHAT COULD BE MORE NATCHERAL. Pants, Gate. Without no pants.

Gate: *Weak.* Oh.

Ma: Oh.

Kid: Oh.

Jake: Stick a fork into a stook an' out run the mice an' then they run up a fellah's pant legs. Had tuh thrash without no pants. Mice had et alla the grain—just straw left. Can't thrash straw.

Ma: *Has turned away—these two old men are hopeless—back to house for more supper material. At door.* Don't forget to wash up, Son. *Kid watching Jake, fascinated, pays no attention.*

Gate: To git back to this here rainmakin'. How did . . .

Jake: Never got away from her.

Gate: Yes you did—you got onto mice and them mice eating them thrashers' pants . . .

Jake: I never said nothing about mice eating anybody's pants—that's ridiculous!

Gate: That's just what I figured. Now about you and this here rainmaking . . .

Jake: I was just explaining how come some folks wasn't so fussy about me raining. Too much moisture. *Reminiscent.* Then too she was a unhealthy sort of a rain I rained—unnatural—folks got all kinds of sickness out of it—colds, flu—why that was the first time I ever had rheumatism in my whole life.

Gate: *Serious.* I'd settle for double pneumonia to get some moisture on that flax of mine. Two hundred acres—dry. *Pause.* Way this here drought weather has been makes a fellow real disgusted to hear you blowing about how you can rain—all about what rainmakers can do with their machines—'nough to give a gopher the heartburn!

Jake: *Hurt.* You don't believe me!

Gate: You bet I don't. Or else you'd rig up your rain machine and then you'd go and you'd rain some!

Jake: I already told you why I quit!

Gate: You ain't told nothin' but a whopping big jag of lies . . . *Pause.* . . . Sheet Lightning Trumper!

Jake: If I wanted to rain—why I could do her right now!

Gate: Who's stopping you! YOU got a crop in! I'm calling you— go on ahead! Bring on your rainmaking machine.

Jake: I ain't got no rain machine made!

Gate: Make her!

Jake: *Pause.* I ain't . . . it ain't that easy . . . I haven't got the . . .

Gate: See what I mean? Just like I said . . .

Jake: You don't make 'em out of anything—got to have the right materials to make a . . .

Gate: Just a whopping jag of—

Jake: *Angry.* Don't say it! I heard what you called me the first time! Do it once more and you won't live to see rain again! *Pause.* I'll rain.

Gate: *Fast.* When?

Jake: Soon as I get my machine put together.

Gate: When'll that be?

Jake: When I'm ready. *Spits.*

Gate: Don't do that!

Jake: What?

Gate: Spitting! Save yer moisture—sinful to waste her like . . .

Jake: *Coldly.* That was fer the flowers there. *Pause.* Thirsty.

Gate: *As he starts for the gate.* Well, whenever you're ready . . .

Kid: Aren't you staying for dinner, Mr. Gatenby . . .

Gate: *Turning at the gate.* Nope. Wasn't ast. *Goes through the gate then heads back.* Pleasant conversation aids the digestion. That hired man you ma's—I was to eat opp'site him today—I'd git the ragin' heartburn. *Out the gate just as:*

Ma: *Enters from house with coffee pot.* Oh—Mr. Gatenby . . .

Kid: Gone home. Said he wasn't asked to dinner.

Ma: Why he doesn't have to be asked. *Turns to Jake seated at table with knife and fork held upright in readiness for the meal.* Seemed to me you two were building up for trouble all morning. I hope you haven't hurt his feelings, Jake.

Jake: Mmmmh.

Ma: What does that mean? Yes—or no?

Jake: Means mmmh.

Ma: *A little angrily.* Jake—isn't it bad enough with that wind oven hot breathing off the prairie—crops turning brown around their edges—the well gone dry—don't you think a little cheerfulness wouldn't be out of place?

Jake: Mmmh.

Ma: Especially at meal times—pleasant conversation . . .

Kid: *Finishing the old song for her.* Aids the digestion.

Ma: That's right. Potatoes, Son.

Kid: I don't feel so hungry, Ma.

Ma: No dessert if you don't eat your . . .

Kid: I don't feel like no pie either . . .

Ma: Any pie . . . *Aside.* . . . Ready for your tea, Jake?

Jake: Uh.

Ma: Part of them anyway, Son—what's getting into you two? Your appetite falling off and Jake . . .

Jake: I'm all right.

Kid: I'm just not so hungry—not fussy about potatoes this kind of weather . . .

Ma: Weather hasn't anything to do with your eating potatoes . . .

Kid: Potatoes are starchy and hot weather . . .

Jake: Do what your ma says . . .

Kid: Miss Henchbaw says . . .

Jake: Her!

Kid: Well . . . in Hygiene she said . . .

Jake: What she know about hygiene . . .

Kid: She teaches it and she . . .

Jake: Just because she teaches it don't mean she knows nothing about it.

Kid: Well . . . she said . . .

Jake: Who cares what she said! Have some potatoes.

Kid: Don't see you eatin' any.

Ma: That's enough Son.

Kid: What's he telling me to eat mine when he isn't having . . .

Ma: All right . . . all right . . . just some of them.

Jake: *Muttering.* Henchbaw— *Mimicking the Kid.* Miss Henchbaw says this, Miss Henchbaw says that, why I can show you more hygiene up a Gosh Hawk's . . .

Ma: *Fast.* I guess this dry weather's getting on everyone's nerves a little.

Kid: *A little vindictively.* Won't have it long. Jake's going to make a rainmaking machine.

Jake: *Lets fork fall with loud clatter.* If a person would keep his mouth shut—he wouldn't get into so much trouble!

Kid: Why I just told Ma what you told Old Man Gatenby this morn—

Ma: *Mister* Gatenby, Son.

Jake: Not that he won't have him a crop of trouble anyways, but maybe if he keeps his mouth shut she won't go so many bushels to the acre. *Pushes chair back.* And maybe she won't grade so high when he get her. *Strides to door.* Number one hard. *Opens door.* Don't you forgit that, Kid. *Pause.* Like I done this mornin'! *Exit.*

Scene 2

Morning again. Jake is down by the shed, has a piece of paper against the side, a stub of a pencil with which he is writing. Muttering not too distinctly . . .

Jake: Two lightnin' rods. *Dives into shed, comes out with two lightning rods which he checks off his list.* Uh—set 'em up about four foot apart—that gas motor outa the chop house . . .

Kid: *Calling from in the house.* Jake!

Jake: *Crossing to the porch, lightning rods under his arm.* Now what would a fellah use for a base—got to have her so's she'll move around easy—got to have . . .

Kid: *Appearing in doorway.* Jake!

Jake: *Sitting down on porch step.* Don't bother me, Kid.

Kid: *Coming and sitting beside Jake.* You workin' out that machine?

Jake: Mmmh.

Kid: What you gonna build her . . .

Jake: *Holding up lightning rods.* Lightnin' rods.

Kid: Two.

Jake: Four—mebbe four—one at each corner—say—there's that old radio cabinet your ma's— *Down to a mutter.* Blue bulbs off of that rheumatism machine . . .

Kid: *Unfolding newspaper.* I was just lookin' . . . the *Crocus Breeze* here, Jake, an' I run acrosst the funniest thing here . . .

Jake: *Engrossed in his figgering. Long pause.* Maybe four lightnin' rods . . . one at each corner . . . that there old radio cabinet . . . *Indistinct muttering.*

Kid: Here in the *Crocus Breeze*—in the part where folks write in about critters that are sick and how to can vegetables . . .

Jake: *Mutter . . . mutter.* Stick a wire . . .

Kid: There's a letter from a fellow— *Obviously reading.* Dear Editor of Diseases and Complaints in Cattle, Horses, and Poultry: I have a cow. She is Holstein-tested for T.B. and Bangs disease. Freshened August fifth. For two years now she has been breathing heavy with a wheezy sound. The last six months she has been sneezing, it sounds just like sneezing, sometimes as many as seven in a row. Her milk is good, she is a very good milker. Is it asthma? Harold Belterlaben, R.R. Four, Broomhead, Sask. *Pause.* Jake . . . can a cow critter have asthma?

Jake: *Mutter . . . mutter.*

Kid: *Sighs.* Weak, tired, nervous, pepless men and women . . . Get new vim, vigor, vitality . . . *Still reading.* Annual meeting of Crocus Pioneer Eastern Star—pot luck supper six o'clock sharp . . . roll call. *Pause.* My favourite recipe . . . Jake . . .

Jake: *Still muttering . . .* blue bulbs . . .

Kid: Hm . . . Notice . . . Municipal District of Crocus Number 31 on August 29th Jake SHEET LIGHTNING TRUMPER will give a demonstration of . . . HEY, JAKE!

Jake: *Breaks off muttering.* Now look here . . .

Kid: Gate! It's Gate . . . he's gone and put a notice in the paper—all about you making a machine and . . .

Jake: Give me that paper! *Reading.* Notice—Municipal Dist . . . will give a demonstration . . . my God . . . he went and done it!!

Kid: What are you going to do, Jake?

Jake: *Pause.* Only one thing to do.

Kid: What?

Jake: Go right on ahead with the machine.

Kid: You started her?

Jake: Started her? I bin buildin' on her for three days now.

Kid: Where, Jake? Where you got her?

Jake: Shed there.

Kid: She all finished, Jake?

Jake: *Getting up.* Nope. These here lightnin' rods got to be tied into her . . . blue bulbs off of my rheumatism machine . . . gas motor outa the chop house.

Kid: *Following Jake across to shed.* Can I have a look at her, Jake—can . . .

Jake: *Slapping paper.* This here—this here thing about me bein' a rainmaker and about me makin' a machine—it—Kid—I guess there's worse things than havin' folks laugh at you . . .

Gate has appeared in the gate right.

Jake: But I don't know what the hell they are!

Gate: *Cheery.* Jake—Kid—just dropped over . . .

Jake and Kid both eye him coldly for long pause.

Jake: Yeah.

Gate: *A little flustered.* Uh—um—dropped over.

Jake: So you did.

Gate: I—uh—figgered to borrow your post-hole auger.

Jake: Did you now.

Gate: Yeah. Oh—and about that there machine of yours—lot of folks been asking me when she'll be ready. August Petersen figured his crop's only good for another week—Lee Tincher . . .

Jake: *Stung.* I'm working on her. I'm working on her!

Gate: *Sly.* Well, it would be kind of nice to see something. *Pause.* If you have anything . . . that is . . .

Jake: I have.

Gate: Where?

Jake: In here. *To shed.*

Gate: *Long pause.* Weeeell now . . . what sort of a critter is that!

Jake: Rain machine.

Gate: You call that there a rain machine?

Jake: Sure do. Ain't got her perfected yet . . .

Gate: Turn her on.

Jake: Can't.

Gate: Why not?

Jake: *Pause.* She's set for hail.

Gate: Is she now?

Jake: She is.

Gate: Well then . . . onset her.

Jake: Can't.

Gate: Why can't you?

Jake: That's what ain't perfected yet. All ready to go 'cept for that one little bug in her. I ain't bringing down no hail on . . .

Gate: Say! Them bulbs . . . them two flat blue bulbs . . . ain't them sort of familiar . . .

Jake: *Hastening to shut him up.* That there's the self same machine I used Manyberries way when I brought rain in ought two. She worked then. She'll work again. Sure dry in ought two— had this drought skinned a mile. *Beginning to roll.* Not a slough in the district—just dust. Seen the frogs settin' up to their eyes in dust—just their two bump eyes showin' . . .

Gate: Them two blue bulbs . . . ain't they off of . . .

Jake: *Hastily.* All over the prairie where the sloughs used to be— little puffs of dust—frogs diving in. You'd see a frog jump— there'd be a plop of dust—then you'd see him swimming the way a frog does—underdust swimming. *Poetical.* Hear them croaking in their dust spring nights was kind of nice—make a fellow remember . . .

Gate: Them two blue bulbs is right off of your old rheumatism . . .

Jake: *Fast again.* Then she got really dry—them winds licking up the top soil—piling it against the fences and the houses and the barns and the granaries—first thing we know there wasn't a speck of dust left in them poor frogs' sloughs . . . kind of tragical the way they died . . . lack of dust.

Gate: *Doom.* When—do you intend to rain?

Jake: They'd got so used to swimming around in that there dust . . . oh . . . why . . . end of this week . . . beginning of the next. *Long pause.* Friday.

Gate: *Triumph.* That's all I wanted to know. *Exit.*

Jake: *Staring after Gate.* Kid . . .

Kid: Yeah, Jake?

Jake: She looks real bad, Kid.

Kid: Gee, Jake—maybe she'll—Reverend Cameron he had a prayin' for rain Sunday last week—he's gonna have another try at her this Sunday—maybe she'll . . .

Jake: Uh - uh.

Kid: You worried, Jake—about next Friday? You think she'll really make rain?

Jake: 'Tain't a rainmakin' machine.

Kid: But you told Gate . . .

Jake: She's a rain machine. Ain't no machine can *make* rain—that's plump silly! Just bring her down if she's up there.

Kid: *Pause.* Jake?

Jake: Yeah?

Kid: Those blue bulbs—Old Gate said . . .

Jake: Don't pay no attention to what he says.

Kid: But they look a lot like your rheum . . .

Jake: Kid—when you say your "Now I lay me down" tonight, after that part about blessing folks, stick in about sending a bunch of grey cloud Friday.

Kid: Okay, Jake.

Curtain

Scene 3

Centre stage the machine is set up. It is magnificent with four lightning rods at the corners—a flimsy framework over it and that draped with red, white and blue bunting. Jake is tinkering with it, the Kid down on his haunches, watching. From time to time during the beginning of this scene both cast a glance up to the clear sky above.

Kid: Kind of melted away, Jake.

Jake: *Engrossed in adjusting the machine.* Yeh.

Kid: When I rolled out of bed she was dark clear to the horizon.

Jake: Don't mean a thing, Kid—han' me that wrench.

Kid: *Handing Jake the wrench.* I kind of thought you wouldn't even have to turn her on at all.

Jake: She's clouded up like that a dozen time, Kid—don't mean a thing. *Looking around.* Folks don't seem very interested in . . .

Kid: More 'n Dominion Day, Twenty-fourth all rolled into one— must be couple hunderd . . .

Jake: Couple hunderd!

Kid: Bin gatherin' whilst you worked on the machine. Mr. Tincher he organized some kids' races an' they're all down by the crick—what's left of her. Stevie Kiziw won the egg an' spoon race. Just about finished—they're comin', Jake . . .

Jake: *Straightening up.* Yeah—I was afraid . . .

Several more townspeople have appeared upstage of the shed, more by the gate right stage.

Jake: *To Kid.* Looks like they're comin', Kid. *To the people crowding from either side.* Folks.

Crowd: Jake . . . 'Day . . . Gonna rain, Jake?

Jake: *Standing up, wiping his hands on a rag.* That's right. Jist make yerselves comfortable— *Looks up to the sky.* I—uh—

Man in crowd: *In audience that is.* Sheet Lightnin' Trumper, folks . . .

2nd man in audience: Runnin' on the Conservative ticket.

3rd man: Come on, come on, let's get rollin' . . .

Jake: All right . . . all right . . . I . . . uh . . . hold her for a minute . . . willyuh . . . like to uh . . . now that you seem to be gathered here in the Kid's ma's front yard . . . like to say a few words . . .

Audience: Rain or shut up!

Jake: All right now—I . . . uh . . . this here is a rain machine. *Pause.* I aim to rain with it. I . . . I ain't gonna explain the principle she works on—rainmakin's like a lot of other things—takes faith—I'd say rainmaking was about one percent machine and ninety-nine percent faith!

Voice 1: Forget the hot air and get on to the rain!

Gate: 'Tain't more wind we want.

Crowd laughter.

Jake: All right—all right—you can laugh—but she won't work without faith! No more'n she'll work without gas. I got to have your faith—all the faith in this here district! It's got to grow out of you folks wanting the rain I'm gonna bring. You got to want her— you got to want to smell her cool on the air. You got to want to hear her—slapping loud on the roof. Filling up them thirsty cracks in your land. Slopping out of your goddam stock troughs—filling and rising in your sloughs and wells. I got to have faith from the women folk too. You got to want me to rain as bad as you want pansies looking up at you from your flower beds—just as bad as sweet peas is thirsty and hollyhocks is thirsty for something besides soapy throw-out water—as bad as you want— *Aside.* Turn her over Kid.—I'm gonna rain and you know I'm gonna rain because she's ten times easier to know I'm gonna than she is to know I ain't.

Kid pantomimes sending off rocket. Crowd's eyes all travelling upwards. Sighs and exclamations.

Jake: You know her in your heart and in your soul and in your gizzard! You know her—if I was you I'd take and put something over my head, Mrs. Totcoal!

Second and third rockets with attendant crowd responses.

You know she's gonna rain and you know her clear as spring water. Any of you folks has snuffy horses—get a good holt on them lines!!

Fourth rocket. Crowd again.

I want your faith an' I'm gonna git it! Stan' well back, folks—git a holt of your kids—for I aim to rain— You keep your eyes glued to them sparks twistin' an' wrigglin' between them aytomic bulbs on that there modern Jake Trumper rain machine—jist watch them rain cree-atin' rockets trailin' their fire-tails untuh the sky . . . Them is lightnin' rods there, folks—an' that motor chuggin' along is pullin' an drawin' at that moisture up there in them grey clouds just like suckin' pop through a straw an' out of a bottle . . .

The machine's motor coughs and cuts out. This might be worked most easily and quickly with someone's gasoline lawn mower laid flat; these usually have a cut-off that works by grounding the motor. Kid quite easily can reach over and cut the motor in and finally off.

Jake has ended his harangue with arms outstretched, stands for long moments then slowly lowers his arms—nothing has happened—obviously he is now beaten.

Falteringly. Well . . . I guess . . . that's her, folks.

Crowd noises begin. Baby starts to cry. Crowd builds. Car horn honks. Some snickers.

Woman: *Distant.* Herschel, Herschel, you come here! Is it all over, Joe—ain't he going to rain . . .

Voice 1: Told you it was just a lot of hot air.

Child: I don't feel no rain—I don't see no rain—when's it going to . . .

Voice 2: Shut up your whining—get into the wagon box . . .

Woman: I told you it was a lot of foolishness before you ever . . .

Voice 2: Don't go blaming it onto me.

Voice 1: Hook up them traces, Virgil—better get headed home . . .

Gate: Just a lot of superstitious damn foolishness—no rain machine never brought no . . .

Sound. Crack and roll of thunder.

Weaker. I say no rain machine never brought no rain to . . .

Sound. Another crack and roll of thunder.

Still weaker. No rain never . . .

Sound. Rain coming sudden with a rush like wind through trees.

Woman: Herschel—Herschel—you come here—come into the car—you want to get your death of cold—soaked!

Sound. Long whoop of delight from one man. Cheering of crowd.

Voice 2: The Lord be praised.

Gate: The Lord nothing—Sheet Lightnin' Trumper.

Crowd on stage all looking up now.

Man 1: I never seen no rain start like this before.

Man 2: She jist up an' let go all of a sudden . . .

Man 3: Soaked . . . hey, Pete—that there dust on yer face has turned tuh mud . . .

Man 4: Lilly—git intuh the house there—your dress is all plastered agin yuh indecent—like you bin swimmin' in yer shimmy . . .

Kid: Jake—Jake—aren't yuh comin' into the house—shelter.

Jake: *Amazed as anybody else.* Hell no, Kid—me—I'm jist gonna stand here for a while . . . *Very gentle voice quietly proud and confident.* Figger I'll jist stay out here fer a while with the rest the folks— *Pause.* In MY rain.

■

Melody Meets the Bag Lady
Rex Deverell

*Gina Wilkinson, **Melody**, and Kate Gregg, **Maizie**, in the
Globe Theatre's schools tour of 1982.*

photograph: Richard Gustin

Melody Meets the Bag Lady was first produced by the Globe Theatre of Regina, Saskatchewan for its Fall, 1982 schools tour with the following cast:

Ivan ——————————————— Stephen Fielden
Sarah ——————————————— Laurel Paetz
Melody——————————————— Gina Wilkinson
Maizie——————————————— Kate Gregg

Requests for performance rights should be addressed to:

Rex Deverell
2775 Broder Street
Regina, Saskatchewan
Canada   S4N 3T8

Scene 1: The Classroom

Melody, Sarah and Ivan are seated at their desks. Preedy, the teacher, may not actually materialize—remaining a goddess on high.

Preedy: Class! Class!

Children: *Together.* Yes, Miss Preedy.

Preedy: Have you all chosen your projects?

Children: Yes, Miss Preedy.

Preedy: Very good, class . . .

Melody rises and speaks to the audience. Her voice overlaps the teacher's.

Melody: Hello everyone. The name of this play is "Melody meets the Bag Lady". I'm Melody Fleming—so this is my play. You might say I am the star.

Preedy: *Overlapping Melody.* Who wants to go first? Sarah?

Sarah: *Standing.* Yes, Miss Preedy?

Preedy: Tell the class what you plan to do for your project.

Sarah: I'm planning to write a story, Miss Preedy.

Melody: That's Sarah. She's one of my best friends.

Preedy: And what will be the theme of your story, Sarah?

Melody: That's because she has so many problems . . .

Sarah: I'm not sure. I thought I'd just write about anything that popped into my head.

Melody: She tells me all her little problems and I try to solve them for her because I'm such a nice person . . .

Sarah: But nothing's really popped yet.

Melody: Look about you, Sarah. There are stories all around you!

Sarah: There are?

Preedy: Melody is quite right. Even the flowers and the trees have stories.

Melody: *To us.* See?

Preedy: Go to the park, Sarah. Watch a young child with a dog— or a little old lady, perhaps . . .

Sarah: The one in the park?

Preedy: Yes?

Sarah: Oh, I know about her. She's a dingbat!

Melody: Once again Sarah misses the point.

Sarah: *To Melody.* I did not!

Preedy: Ivan?

Ivan: *Who has been daydreaming.* Yes, Miss Preedy?

Melody: And that's my other friend, Ivan.

Preedy: What will your project be, Ivan?

Ivan: Project?

Melody: Ivan's mind is often somewhere else.

Ivan: Oh—project! Could I do another science project, Miss Preedy?

Melody: Usually on something scientific. Ivan's an inventor.

Preedy: If you wish. What is it this time?

Ivan: I'm working on this invention? It's called a Habit Remover. Like if you've got this bad habit like maybe chewing your finger nails—well you'd press a button on the machine and presto—you wouldn't have the habit any more.

Melody: He can't make a machine that'll do that!

Sarah: Sure he can. Even I could.

Everybody turns to her.

Ivan: How?

Sarah: You get this box see? And you've got some kind of a saw inside, right? And you put your hand in and you press the button and the saw cuts off your fingers and you can't bite your fingernails any more because you don't have any, right?

Preedy: And Melody, what is your project to be?

Melody: *Archly.* My project is in the social studies area. As everyone knows I plan to be a social worker when I grow up and I am going to start now. I shall . . . (are you ready?) . . . I shall completely change somebody's life.

Ivan: Whose?

Melody: Could be anybody: somebody who is a little weird. I'll change them back into a normal human being.

Ivan: I've got a frog in my lunchpail—you want to start on that?

Sarah: Yeah—kiss it and turn it into a prince.

Melody: I'm not going to kiss any frog—this is serious. I'm going to use only proven social-psychological techniques.

Ivan: Come along, Herr Frog. Lie down on der couch. Tell me everrytink dot bozzers you. You are not really a frog, mein little froggy, nein, nein. You are Prince! You hear? Prince! Now schtopp hoppink around undt behafe like der prince. *As chaos breaks out.* I said schtopp hoppink!

Preedy: *Restoring order.* That's enough, children. I know all of you are excited by your projects but remember you are still in school . . .

Sarah: *Aside.* How could we forget?

Preedy: They are all very interesting projects. Each of you will draw up a report and have it on my desk by Friday . . .

Everybody groans. "Friday? Oh no, not Friday! Give us a break!" etc.

Preedy: Yes, Friday. Class dismissed.

Exit Preedy. Everybody gathers books, talking all at once.

Sarah: How am I going to write a story by Friday—I don't know what to write about! Aaaargh!

Ivan: This is a major invention. These things take time!

Sarah: Does she think Pippy Longstockings was written in a day?

Ivan: Think of the arithmetic—the computations—it'll take my computer three whole days just to figure out the equations . . .

Melody: All I want to know is—

The others pause and look at her.

Melody: Where do I find my client?

Sarah: Client?

Melody: I have to have a weirdo who needs changing.

Ivan: Don't look at me.

Sarah: Me neither.

Melody: *Wailing.* I'm never going to get done by Friday!

Sarah: I know somebody.

Melody: Who?

Sarah: The dingbat in the park.

Ivan: Oh, come on! Not her!

Sarah: Why not?

Ivan: She's too weird.

Melody: *Stamping her foot.* Who are you talking about?

Sarah: The bag lady! Who else?

Melody looks blank.

Ivan: You've seen her—you musta seen her!

Melody: Nope.

Sarah: With the bags and everything?

Melody: Nope.

Sarah: Well, what are we waiting for. Let's go and see the dingbat in the park!

All exit.

Scene 2: The Park

Enter Maizie, a vigorous, shabbily dignified, slightly manic old lady. She has been around a long time and a lot. She may be wise or she may be crazy. Pinned to her coat are several large buttons bearing such messages as "Motorcycle to Tanzania", "The Rabbit Warren Society", "The Monsoon Relief Fund", "The Emergency Aid Org.", "Friends of Samoa", "Save the Whales", "The Inuit Centre", "Smile". Around her shoulders and in her hands are a myriad of bags packed with a lifetime of wanderings. Under her coat is an outlandish garb—almost clownlike in its effect. She is weird alright—but joyfully so.

Maizie: *Singing.* Oh what a beautiful morning
It was—but isn't any more because it is the afternoon now.
Oh, what a wonderful day
Everything's been goin' my way
And it's gonna keep on going my way
Wait an' see if it don't.
Calling to the world. Hello World! Hello! Hello Sky! Hello Trees! Hello Birds! Hello Wind! Hello Grass! Hello Sky! Did I say hello to you already? I did? Sorry—There's one cloud—one fluffy little thing. Hello Cloud. Hello People! Are there any people? No people?—Come and say hello to the world! The world never gets said hello to—*Launching into an oration.* The world never gets a simple word of greeting and it's about time it did. Yes, time it did! We say hello to each other. When we meet somebody we say— Hello, pleased to meet you, how are you? But we never say it to the sky. Why not? The sky has as much right as anybody. *To the sky.* Haven't you? Yes he has. Or she has. *To the sky.* Which are you? *Surprised.* Oh! *Continuing.* We never say it to the trees or the wind—and yet *Dramatically* these things are always with us! Yes!

And the air we breathe! Hello Air. We know these brothers and sisters better than our own family—yet we don't care enough to give them the time of day, do we? *Suddenly.* Hello, birdies!

Meanwhile Sarah and Ivan have led Melody into the park. They watch Maizie from a hiding place.

Sarah: That's her!

Maizie dips, searches through her bags. In the process we get to see some of the odd items they contain: an ancestral portrait, a doily, a toaster, an iron, a roll of toilet paper, a pair of mukluks, an oriental fan, a hot water bottle, a can of ravioli, . . . and more.

Maizie: No . . . no . . . was it this one? No . . . ah, yes. *She produces a bag of bread crumbs.* Here birdy, birdy! *Chirping sounds.* Here, birdy! *Scattering the crumbs.* Nice birdy . . .

Ivan: She's off with the birds . . .

The children are trying to stop from giggling.

Melody: Shhh!

Maizie: Come down and get your dindin . . .

Ivan: Tweet, tweet!

The children can not contain themselves any longer. There is a chorus of choked giggles.

Maizie: What?

Outright laughter.

Maizie: *Caught short.* Laughing? Where is that coming from? Aha! From that garbage can!

The garbage can moves.

It's moving! *More giggles.* Oho—there's something behind the garbage can. What would I like it to be? *Pause—she looks up.* I know—a cloud—a cloud that pushes garbage cans.

Sarah: You'll never be able to make her normal.

Melody: Oh no?

Maizie: Come out, come out—wee cloudy . . .

Sarah: You'll never do it, not in a thousand years.

Melody: Just watch me.

Melody strides out and confronts Maizie.

Maizie: Ah!

Melody: You ought to be ashamed of yourself!

Maizie: *Startled.* Pardon?

Melody: You heard me. I said you ought to be ashamed of yourself.

Maizie: Are you sure you are a cloud?

Melody: What are you going to do about it?

Maizie: About . . . ?

Melody: About your life! About changing your life!

Maizie: *Alarmed.* Oh my goodness! What's wrong with it? *She tries to look at herself.*

Melody: It isn't normal.

Maizie: *Amazed.* Not normal?

Melody: You talk funny. What's in all those bags?

Maizie: Everything I own.

Melody: That's stupid. Why don't you leave it at home?

Maizie: This is my home.

Melody: *Amazed.* This park?

Maizie: Sure. Here, there, wherever I am!

Melody: That's disgusting. Where do you go to the bathroom?

Maizie: I use the public lavatories.

Melody: That's disgusting. You should live inside—under a roof someplace—someplace with a bathroom.

Maizie: You don't talk like a cloud.

Melody: What makes you think I'm a cloud?

Maizie: I don't know! You are, though, aren't you?

There are great hoots of laughter as Sarah and Ivan roll out of their hiding place clutching their stomachs.

Melody: No! I'm Melody.

Maizie: A melody!

Melody: No! That's my name!

Maizie: Amazing!

Melody: What's so amazing?

Maizie: That you look exactly like a little girl and that you have such a musical name. Very unusual for a cloud!

Melody: I'm Melody Fleming, a girl. *Pointing to the others.* Ask them!

Maizie: *Seeing the others.* Delightful! The whole sky has come to play with me! *Examining Sarah.* You look like a star—are you a star?

Sarah: Well . . .

Maizie: You're very twinkly! *To Ivan.* Now, you could be sunshine . . .

Ivan: *Embarrassed.* This is dumb.

Maizie: Oh—no more sunshine . . . so sorry.

Melody: That's Ivan and that's Sarah. Ask them if I'm a cloud.

Maizie: *To the others.* Is she?

Ivan: *Thinking.* Yeah.

Sarah: Yeah, she is actually.

Melody: *Betrayed.* You guys!

Maizie: I thought so.

Sarah and Ivan collapse once more.

Sarah: You'll never make her normal, not in a thousand years.

Ivan: And you've only got until Friday! Hahahahaheehahehahe!

Sarah: Hahehehahehahehahehaheha!

Melody: *To Maizie.* See that?

Maizie nods.

Melody: You know who they're laughing at, don't you.

Maizie: Laughter is the best sound in the world.

Melody: *Reality therapy.* They are laughing at you.

Maizie: *Trying to understand.* At me?

Melody: Yes, at you.

Maizie: That's alright, I guess.

Melody: It is not 'alright'—they think you're crazy.

Maizie: Crazy?

Melody: So what are you going to do about it?

Maizie: *To the other children.* Do you think I'm crazy?

Sarah and Ivan sober up.

Sarah: *Accusingly.* Melody!

Ivan: No, no. Of course not.

Maizie: *Bluntly.* Tell me the truth.

Ivan: Well, you do act a little strange.

Sarah: Just a little.

Melody: Just a lot.

Maizie is silent.

Sarah: And you've got all those funny buttons . . .

Maizie: These are the things I believe in.

Sarah: *Chagrined.* Oh.

Maizie: Take this one—"Motorcycle to Tanzania." Nobody has done it before. Nobody has ever thought of motorcycling to Tanzania. Why not, I ask you? I ask you, why not!? Is it because people don't know where Tanzania is exactly? Well, it's time we found out, isn't it? People live there, don't they? How would you feel if Tanzanians didn't know where you were. And what about "Save the Whales", eh? There's something to fight for. And I say if you don't have something to fight for, then you're nothing!

Ivan: Right on!

Sarah: Right!

Melody: No—wrong. Are you happy?

Maizie: Oh. *Pause.* Sure. *Pause.* Of course . . . as long as I have the sky and the earth, the wind and the birds . . . and friends . . .

Melody: *Fastening on.* Friends?

Maizie: Yes.

Melody: Where are they?

Maizie: *Stumped.* I don't know. I used to have some, I think. *To the three of them.* Will you be my friends?

Ivan and Sarah: Sure.

Melody: *Getting the others into a huddle.* No! This is crucial. You can't be—not until she reforms.

Sarah: Aw, c'mon . . .

Ivan: Give the poor lady a break . . .

Melody: If you really want to be her friends—help me. *The others hesitate.* Good, I'll do the talking. *To Maizie.* All right. No friends.

Maizie: *More disappointed than she wants to admit.* Oh! Well, I've been lonely before. I suppose I can put up with it.

Melody: *Brusquely.* Good. *To Ivan and Sarah.* Come on.

The children set off, leaving the bag lady alone.

Maizie: *Suddenly.* Wait!

The children turn back to her.

Maizie: What do you want me to do?

Melody: *Triumphant.* Don't worry about a thing. I'll take care of you!

Maizie: You?

Melody: Trust me! Meet me here every day. By Friday you'll be as normal as I am.

Maizie: *To the others.* And you'll be my friends?

Sarah: Sure . . .

Ivan: Sure thing.

Sarah: Yeah . . .

But an element of nervousness has crept into the project.

Ivan: *To Melody as the children exit.* So now we helped you, you gotta help us!

Sarah: Yeah, what am I going to do for my story, eh?

Ivan: Can you help me get parts for my Habit Remover?

Melody: Sure, sure. *Turning back to Maizie.* Don't forget—uh—what's your name?

Maizie: Maizie.

Melody: Don't forget, Maizie, same place—same time.

Maizie waves a little goodbye as the children go. Maizie is now alone with the audience. She shifts through her belongings morosely.

Maizie: *To the audience.* I have a funny feeling. Not funny-funny. Funny-awful. I don't think I'm going to like this. *Pause.* "Normal." What's normal? Being the same as everybody else? Being like you people? But you don't all look the same. Nobody's exactly the same—everybody's face is different or we couldn't tell each other apart. Of course, a lot of you are wearing blue jeans. *Or whatever the popular uniform happens to be.* Maybe if I wore blue jeans . . . When I was a little girl I always dressed the same as everybody else—until one day I decided to wear what I liked. So I showed up in school with a green shawl I found in a junk pile and a pair of big pants with yellow stripes and red polkadots . . . and a funny hat. Do you think anybody laughed at me? They did. All my classmates laughed themselves silly. But the next day not as many people laughed and the day after that nobody laughed. But nobody played with me, either. So I gave it up. But it was fun, wearing whatever I wanted—being whatever I wanted, strange or not—and I kept it in my head, you see. Then one day, when I was grown, it all came out and look at me now! And do you know what? I can have so much fun!

Special sequence of audience participation:

Would you like to know what goes on in my imagination? Shut

your eyes and tell me the first thing that pops into your mind. *Maizie becomes a kind of creative drama teacher. She uses audience's suggestions to create a scene with participation. Use the following as a model.*

A train!! Oh, I've been on so many trains—real ones, imaginary ones—sometimes I even try to be a train. Oooooooooh! Train whistles. Oooooooh! Old steam locomotive. Ooooooooh! All aboard! Boooooooaaaaaard!! Chuff, chuff, chuff, chuffchuff, chuffchuff, chuffachuffachuffachuffachuff *Picking up momentum.* chchchchchchchchchchchch-oooooooooooooh-chchchchchchchchchc Tickets please, tickets please. *To audience member.* May I have your ticket, sir? Thank you. Where are you going Ma'am? Oh, imagine that! Nice place, they say. Never been there myself. Oh, we've got an emergency here in the front seat, lady looking a little sick. Have we a doctor on the train . . . Anybody know any first aid . . . Doctor—anything the rest of us can do to help . . . Eeeeeeech— Yes—I know the train has stopped—I'm busy here—anybody want to go up to the engine and see what's wrong? . . . Brace yourselves— the brakes have let go! We're about to go down the side of a mountain . . . chchchchchchchchchchchcchchchccchch . . . . ooooooh!!! . . . *Everything builds to a great climax of fun and terror. Maizie collapses from exhaustion.*

(Special note: The secret of this participation is to begin by getting enough audience suggestions to choose productive ones. Begin with easy and physically small movement, and immediately think of a danger that might occur in relation to the topic.)

Oh, enough of that. I'll have to say goodbye to that sort of stuff. I want to have friends, see . . . *Confiding.* 'cause sometimes I'm not this happy. Somctimes I feel very, very . . . bad. And that's when I need friends and I can't always find them. So I'll change. I'll try to be normal . . . whatever that is. *Pause.* I suppose Melody will tell me. *She begins to leave.* I would've like it better if she'd been a cloud.

Scene 3: Ivan's Basement

Ivan: *Calling up the stairway.* Okay, Mom. I'll be up in a minute. *To the audience.* Being a boy inventor isn't all that great, you know what I mean. Oh, being an inventor is great—I've invented some really neat things. But being my age and being an inventor is difficult. Like, I get into a problem and I'm just ready to come up with the answer and what happens? My mother says *Imitating her.* "It's time to go to bed now, Ivan." All I might need is another five minutes or maybe ten and I'd have the most brilliant discovery of the century! But no—I have to go to bed. And the next morning, I have to go to school and then by the time I get back to it I've forgotten where I was and maybe it wasn't such a big deal and maybe I've gotten interested in something else. Like once I was almost sure I could invent a time machine so I could go back into history or travel into the future? What happened? My mother yells down "Your Auntie Harriet is here. Come up and visit like a good boy." "But Mom!" "Ivan!" "Alright, Mom." So I go up and visit Auntie Harriet and she's okay but I'd rather have visited King Arthur or maybe even a dinosaur.

He hears another request from overhead.

I'm coming right away. *To us.* Anyway, I've gotta go to bed now and I haven't even started on my Habit Remover and I'm going to need a lot of help in the morning—would you be able to help me? *Of course we will—Ivan is relieved.* Oh, that's good! If you can think up some ideas—we'll work on it in the morning okay? *Upstairs.* Coming!

Scene 4: Sarah's Bathroom

Sarah enters ready for bed, carrying her toothbrush.

Sarah: *Imitating Melody.* "Look about you, Sarah. There are stories all around you!" Sure. Where are they then? "Even the flowers and the trees have stories." Sure. What stories? The Story of Trees: They get planted and they grow and they just sit there. Every Fall they drop their leaves. Every Spring they grow new ones. The End. Exciting. *She brushes furiously.* Melody has got her victim to reform, Ivan has his machine to build—everybody's got their project except me. Me, I've got nothin'. I'd sooner be the bag lady. Least she doesn't have to do projects. She probably doesn't have to brush her teeth, either. *Leaving.* She probably never has to go to the dentist, even . . .

Exits sleepily.

Scene 5: The Next Day in the Park

Melody is pacing up and down impatiently, glancing at her watch every few seconds.

Melody: So where is she? Twenty minutes late already. Oooh, she's not going to come and I won't be able to do my project. I shoulda known better than to count on her. Boy that's one habit I hope Ivan can remove with his machine—nothing makes me madder than lateness. Especially if I have to wait. You'd think if a person had a chance to change their whole life, the least they could do is be on time.

She sees Maizie approaching and calls to her.

Where were you!

Maizie: *Innocently.* Here.

Melody: No you weren't.

Maizie: Yes I was.

Melody: I was here!

Maizie: That's right and I'm here.

Melody: But you were supposed to be here!

By now Maizie has reached Melody.

Maizie: I am here!

Melody: Oooh . . . I haven't hardly any time left. Lie down on that bench.

Maizie: Alright. *She does so and promptly falls asleep.*

Melody: Now, Maizie . . . Maizie?

Maizie begins to snore.

Melody: No, no! *Maizie wakes up, alarmed*—you're not supposed to go to sleep—you're supposed to tell me your problems.

Maizie: *Frightened.* What problems? No, don't tell me.

Melody: *Amazed.* Pardon?

Maizie: If I've got problems, I don't want to know.

Melody: *Aside.* This is going to be harder than I thought.

Maizie: *Talking to the air.* You don't have any problems . . . and I've always tried to live like you. *Pause. Maizie seems to be hearing something.* What was that you said?

Melody: Who are you talking to?

Maizie: The wind.

Melody: *Reality therapy.* The wind! The wind doesn't talk!

Maizie: Yes it does . . .

Melody: No it doesn't.

Maizie: Listen. Hear it rustling in the leaves? You have to listen in a special way.

Melody: In a crazy way. Maizie, if you are going to be helped you have to give up talking to the wind and the clouds and all that kind of stuff.

Maizie: But wh . . .

Melody: And you have to throw away all those bags . . .

Maizie: *Weakly.* No!

Melody: And those silly buttons . . .

Maizie: They aren't silly.

Melody: They are, Maizie. And get rid of those awful clothes . . .

Maizie: What'll I wear?

Melody: A sensible pantsuit from Woolco.

Maizie: I can't!

Melody: You know what your problem is?

Maizie: What?

Melody: You don't want to change badly enough.

Maizie: I want to, Melody, but it's too hard for me. I mean I want friends and I don't want people to laugh at me (though I can put up with that like always) but I don't want to give up anything either—I mean I want to but I don't. See?

Pauses.

Melody: *Decisively.* Torture.

Maizie: *Yelp.* No!

Melody: Yes.

Maizie: I can't stand pain!

Melody: It's the only way. It's the oldest method to effect social change and it may be the best. Give me your thumb.

Excruciating thumb twisting.

Melody: *Finally.* Well?

Maizie: I wish you'd been a cloud.

Melody: You can't live with your head in the clouds all your life, Maizie. Let's face it. "The world is a brutal, ugly, vicious place full of hunger and violence. However if everybody would work hard and wear nice clothes there's no reason we can't be happy." A very great man said that, Maizie.

Maizie: Who?

Melody: My father. Now, get rid of all those bags.

Maizie: Everything I own? This stuff is valuable!

Melody: *Peering into the bags.* This stuff is junk.

Maizie: *With dignity.* Some of it has great sentimental value. *She pulls out the ancestor portrait.*

Melody: Is that your grandfather?

Maizie: Not exactly.

Melody: Either he is or he isn't.

Maizie: Well, he's my adopted grandfather. I adopted him. grandfather.

Melody: Is he still alive?

Maizie: I don't know—I never met him.

Melody: Where did you get his picture?

Maizie: From a garbage dump in Iraq.

Melody: You've never been in Iraq!

Maizie: I've been all over the place.

Melody: What's this? *Strange object.*

Maizie: I used to know what that was. Maybe it's a camel cover. *She tries it on in several ways.* I'm not sure. Interesting, though, isn't it?

Melody: *Abruptly picking up a bag and taking it to the garbage can.* Okay, we'll just get rid of this . . .

Maizie: Wait—I've got my toothbrush in there. *She rescues it from the can.*

Melody: *Picking up another one.* And this . . .

Maizie: Nope—my TV's in that one.

Melody: *Continuing.* And this one—*Doubletake.* Your TV?

Maizie goes to the garbage and pulls a frame with buttons out of her bag. She shows Melody the current network program—i.e. whatever they can see through the frame.

Maizie: My TV. Full colour, three dimensions, all channels—if I don't like what I see on that channel—I switch! *She frames several different views in sequence.* See?

But Melody has started to throw the bags away faster and faster.

Maizie: Hey, not that one!

Maizie fishes the bags out of the garbage as fast as Melody can throw them in. Soon Melody is throwing bags away for the second or third time. Finally she realizes what is happening.

Melody: Maizie!

Maizie looks innocent.

Melody: This is useless. I've got to try something else. *Thinks.* I know! Public ridicule.

Maizie: What's that?

Melody: I'm going to laugh at you until you improve yourself!

Maizie: *Delighted.* Oh good. *Worried.* Do you think it'll work?

Melody: Sometimes it works—sometimes it doesn't.

Maizie: *Fascinated.* Go ahead.

Melody begins to laugh in the most scornful way she can think of. Maizie listens in delight and starts to laugh herself. Trying to be helpful, Maizie clowns with some of her junk—pretending to be her adopted ancestor for instance and using his portrait as a mask—or using the toaster as a hat. Soon everybody is laughing with Maizie rather than at her. Even Melody has to laugh genuinely in spite of herself—but this turns to despair and she begins to weep.

Maizie: What's wrong, Melody?

Melody: This isn't supposed to be funny.

Maizie: Did I do something wrong?

Melody: If you laugh too it won't work. You are supposed to feel awful. . . .

Maizie: *Trying to be helpful.* I could try. *Clutching her stomach and trying to feel agony.* Oh—I feel rotten—I feel so awful . . .

Melody: That's no good. Sarah and Ivan were right. I'll never get you to change—not in a thousand years . . .

Maizie: *Hopefully.* Maybe we'd better give up, eh?

Melody: Yeah. *Jumping up.* No! A Fleming never gives up—never! Will you do anything to change your life?

Maizie: No, I can't say that I would . . .

Melody: *Rephrasing.* Would you do anything to have friends?

Maizie: *After a pause.* Maybe—

Melody: Yes or no?

Maizie: *Uncertainly.* Yes?

Melody: Would you submit to a small scientific experiment?

Maizie: What kind of an experiment?

Melody: Come on!

She grabs Maizie and pulls her off.

Maizie: Where?

Melody: Ivan's house!

And they leave.

Scene 6: Ivan's Basement Lab

Ivan is puttering around with various bits of electronic equipment.

Ivan: *Trying to work himself into a fit of creativity.* Alright, this is the big push—this is it. It's now or never! Now we are going to build the— *Fanfare.* Tuhtra tuhtrraaa Habit Remover. *Pause.* Tuhtraaa! *Pause. He turns to audience.* Any ideas?

If the audience come up with ideas Ivan can use the audience to produce the device—as parts of the machine, as technicians and as designers and consultants. Otherwise go to the following.

Let's work this out step by step. We can use my talking computer.

He twists dials and we hear electronic noises.

Hello, Computer.

Computer Voice: Hello, Ivan.

Ivan: Information mode, please.

Computer Voice: File subject?

Ivan: Human behaviour.

Computer: Continue.

Ivan: Habits.

Computer: Continue.

Ivan: Explain, please.

Computer Voice: Definition: a habit is an automatic function of the brain. The brain tells its user to do x automatically. X is a particular habit. Continue.

Ivan: How do we get a habit?

Computer Voice: The user repeats an action until it is programmed into the brain. Continue.

Ivan: How can habits be changed?

Computer Voice: Reprogram brain. Continue.

Ivan: Like a computer?

Computer Voice: *Patiently.* Ivan, the brain is a computer.

Ivan: That's the answer!

Computer Voice: What answer?

Ivan: Thank you, Computer.

Computer Voice: *Disgruntled.* Nobody ever tells me anything . . .

Ivan turns it off.

Ivan: We need a machine that will send special electric signals to the brain and reprogram a person's bad habits . . . Will you be my machine? Great! What'll we need? A power generator—first of all . . . . This part can be the power generator. What do we need for a power generator . . . ? Wire? Good! Coils of wire turning around and around—switches going off and on—vibrating oscilloscopes—lights flashing on and off—wheels turning—we need some electronic noises. And this part can be the electronic centre that passes information back and forth to the person's brain and generates the right kind of signals and we need wire from the generator to the electronic centre and we need . . .

Gradually Ivan turns the audience into a giant science fiction machine.

Good it's all ready. This'll be the main switch, okay. When I turn it off everything is quiet. When I turn it on the machine comes to life. Here goes. On!

Trial run.

Ivan: *Pulling switch.* Off! *He makes necessary adjustments.* There—it should work. I wonder if it will. I should test it out on myself first I guess. *Switch.* On!

It has been built in such a way that he has to walk through the machine for treatment—like a car wash. As he does so his body begins to vibrate. He emerges and turns the machine off.

Off! There. I don't feel any different. Uh-oh. I'm beginning to feel a little—beep—strange. Er, strange. Beep. Oh—beep, I, beeple beep—I—beep beep beeple beep . . .

The more incoherent he becomes, the happier he is with himself. Melody's voice is heard from overhead.

Melody: Ivan! Ivan! May we come down? Ivan!

Ivan: Beep beep, beeple beep!

Ivan is merrily tottering about the room like a mechanical man gone out of wack.

Melody: Pardon?

Ivan: Beep beep beeple beeple beep.

Melody: I can't understand a word you're saying. *She and Maizie enter.* Ivan!

Maizie: My goodness!

Melody: Is this a joke?

Ivan: Beep, beep, beeple beeple beeple . . .

Melody: What's gotten into him?

The audience may say "It was the machine" or Ivan himself is finally able to indicate what has happened.

What'll we do?

Ivan or the audience indicates that she is to give him another treatment from the machine. Ivan places himself in the machine and signals for Melody to turn it on.

Alright. *Pulling switch.* On!

The machine operates. A restored Ivan emerges in triumph.

Ivan: Aaaaall riiight!!! *Turning the machine off.* Off! Yaaay!

Melody: Your Habit Remover?

Ivan: It works!!!

Maizie: It does?

Melody: Are you sure?

Ivan: It sure removed my habit of speaking in English.

Maizie: I'm very happy for you.

Ivan: *Oblivious.* Thank you.

Melody: Congratulations, Ivan.

Ivan: Thank you.

Melody: *Casually.* I don't suppose you want to make any improvements to that machine, do you?

Ivan: What kind of improvements?

Melody: I don't know—I mean it's a very good machine . . .

Ivan: Right. How could it be improved?

Melody: What if it could remove weirdness?

Ivan: *Intrigued.* Hey! I never thought of that. Well, the principle is the same . . .

Melody: Run her through it!

Ivan: *Shocked.* What?

Maizie: *At the same time.* Me?

Ivan: But . . .

Melody: *Impatiently.* I don't have any time to waste. Tomorrow's Friday already, Okay?

Maizie: *Chickening out.* What's the hurry?

Ivan: The machine is only supposed to get rid of the odd little bad habit—like—picking your nose or—*But his mind is clicking over.* It'd take a lot more power.

Melody: Think, Ivan! If you could get your machine to change people's lives it would be a great blessing for mankind!

Ivan: *He is dubious but tempted.* It would?

Melody: With your machine you could change all the bad people. Think of it: no more smelly people, no more pesky people . . .

Ivan: I don't know, Melody. Something might go wrong. I wouldn't know how to change her back again . . .

Maizie: So we'd better just forget it.

Melody: Don't you want to see if the machine can do it?

Ivan: *Weakening.* Yeah, I do, actually.

Maizie: On the other hand . . .

Ivan: Lemme see—if we just boosted the speed here and made this a little bigger and if we had more juice coming in here . . . *He sets about making the necessary adjustments.*

Maizie: I don't think I'm ready . . .

Melody: Hurry Ivan . . .

Maizie: May I leave now?

Melody: No!

Ivan: That should do it.

Melody ushers Maizie to the machine.

Maizie: I want to change my mind!

Melody: You're going to change everything. And you're going to have all the friends you want.

Maizie: Promise?

Melody: *As she pushes her in.* Sure.

Maizie: Bye . . .

At this moment Maizie is totally vulnerable—she is terrified of the machine—sorrowful over the possibility of losing her past life— but her longing for friendship wins out.

Melody: Give her the juice!

Ivan: *Pulling the switch.* On! *To his power generator.* Alright—we need all the power you've got. *The machine revs up.* More still. *Maizie's body begins to vibrate. Sarah comes down the stairs.*

Sarah: Hi, everybody—what's happening? *Seeing the machine and Maizie inside of it.* Gosh!

Ivan: It's my Habit Remover.

Melody: Only now it's a Person Changer.

Sarah: *Alarmed.* No, don't! You shouldn't. Get her out of there. Turn it off!

Ivan: We can't! Don't touch that switch—it's too late!

Melody: *Pointing at Maizie.* What's it doing to her?

Maizie seems to be undergoing a series of extravagant personality transformations.

Ivan: She's changing!

Sarah: Oh no!

Each personality may repeat a characteristic phrase until the next one takes over.

Ivan: *Whistling in amazement.* Well, whad'ya know! That's amazing! That's great!

Sarah: *Miserably.* Oh, what are we going to do?

Ivan: *Continuing to be enthusiastic.* Pull her out when she's ready.

Melody: Right. *Watching the personality changes.* Okay. Not that one. Nope, Closer. Nope. Maybe. Yucky. Hey, that looks good!

Ivan: *Hand on the switch.* Are you sure?

Melody: Yes! That's the one. Take her out.

Ivan: *Shutting off the machine.* She's all yours.

Maizie pops out of the machine. She has lost all of her glow. She moves rather tightly and at first seems somewhat dazed.

Sarah: *Rushing to her.* Are you alright?

Maizie: Hmmm?

Melody: Well?

Maizie: What am I doing in these awful clothes?

Melody: *Triumphantly.* Aha!

Maizie: Does anyone have the time?

Melody: Aha!

Maizie: *Managing to change some of the more outrageous elements of her costume.* I suppose I'd better do a little shopping and me-oh-my! I don't have any place to live . . . *She begins to leave.*

Melody: *Picking up some of her bags.* Don't forget these.

Maizie: What?

Sarah: Your bags!

Maizie: *Sniffing.* Junk.

Melody: Aha!

Maizie: Yes—a nice room somewhere respectable . . . Oh, I'm going to be so busy . . . finding a room and buying pantsuits and being sensible, it makes me tired just to think about it . . .

She climbs the stairs feeling the weight of the world. The children stare after her. Melody is ecstatic. Ivan has mixed emotions. Sarah is aghast.

Melody: I did it!

Ivan: It worked!

Sarah: That was the dumbest thing you guys ever did!

Melody: What's wrong with you?

Sarah: I liked her the way she was.

Ivan: Now you tell us.

Melody: You're just mad because Ivan and I have our projects finished and tomorrow's Friday and I bet you haven't even started yours.

Sarah: *Frustrated.* Oooooooooooh!!! *And she leaves.*

Ivan: Wait, Sarah . . .

Melody: Let her go, Ivan. She's just a spoilsport. Enjoy your success . . .

Ivan: *He looks at Melody, then at the machine and then turns towards the stairway. Sarah! Exit.*

Melody: Ivan! *To herself.* Success can make people go all strange. *Following Ivan.* Ivan! *Exit.*

Scene 7: The Park

Sarah enters with Maizie's bags.

Sarah: *Calling.* Maizie! Maizie! *No answer.* That's funny. I thought she'd be here for sure. No matter how changed she was you'd think she'd come back to the park, eh? Maizie? Bag lady? *To one of the audience members.* Excuse me, sir. I'm looking for this lady that comes to the park sometimes. You might have seen her— she wears buttons and things? *We may tell Sarah where Maizie is.* Really? Has she been back here since? No? I've got her bags. I was hoping she'd need them. A person can't get rid of everything they own just like that, can they? Okay—if you see her again, tell her I've got her bags, alright?

Ivan: *Entering.* Sarah—

Sarah: Go away. I'm not talking to you. How could you do such a thing to that nice old lady . . .

Ivan: I just wanted to find out if my machine—

Sarah: *Scornfully.* Your machine!

Ivan: . . . my machine could do all that . . .

Sarah: Is that all you ever think about? Whether your gadgets are going to work?

Ivan: Well, it was an interesting problem to solve . . .

Sarah: An interesting problem!

Ivan: A challenge.

Sarah: A chall—

Ivan: Stop repeating what I say . . .

Sarah: What about poor Maizie. She's more than an interesting problem, you know—it was her whole way of living that you were fooling with. You have to think of that, you know!

Ivan: *Reluctantly.* Maybe you're right . . .

Sarah: You're just like Melody.

Melody: *Entering right on cue.* Nobody's just like me—I'm the best . . .

Sarah: *Turning on her.* Sure, sure . . . you were just using that poor lady for your project—you didn't care about her at all . . .

Melody: I did so.

Sarah: No you didn't. Not at all . . .

Ivan: Well you were laughing at her too, Sarah. You don't have to sound so perfect . . .

Melody: That's right. You're the one who called her the dingbat in the park . . .

Sarah: *Chagrined.* I guess I did . . . but . . .

Melody: So don't blame us. Besides—she'll be much better off now that she has turned normal . . .

Ivan: Look.

They look where Ivan is pointing and see Maizie entering. She now has changed to an extraordinarily "normal" costume. The contrast between her present self and her former self is tragic. Even Melody perceives it. Maizie takes out a newspaper and begins to read. She has in fact turned into a standard narrow-vision adult.

Ivan: *Whispering.* Uh oh.

Sarah: See?

Ivan: Yeah.

Melody: No—there's nothing wrong with her.

Sarah: Go be her friend then.

Ivan: Yeah, you promised.

Melody: Alright, but you come with me.

Sarah: Okay . . .

Ivan: Okay . . .

Melody: Okay.

The little group approaches Maizie very tentatively with Melody in the lead.

Melody: Hi, Maizie.

Maizie: *Looking up.* Hello.

Pause. Maizie goes back to her newspaper.

Melody: Have you found a place to live?

Maizie: *Without looking up.* Yes, thank you.

Sarah: *Hopefully.* Is it fun?

Maizie: *As if she has never heard the word.* Fun?

Sarah: *Trying to demonstrate.* Yeah, "fun"!

Maizie: My room is modest but practical, thank you.

Sarah: *Sober.* Oh.

Melody: How do you feel?

Maizie: Fine, thank you.

Pause.

Ivan: It's a nice day, isn't it?

Maizie: Is it? *She looks around her vaguely.* I suppose it might be. *Back to the newspaper.*

The children look at each other—having run out of conversation starters.

Maizie: Did you children have anything in particular you wanted?

They are stung at being called children.

Melody: Don't—don't you want us for your friends?

Maizie: Of course I do, kiddies . . .

Sarah: Kiddies!

Maizie: Now perhaps you could run along and play and let Auntie Maizie read her paper.

Sarah: Where are your buttons?

Maizie: Oh, those silly things—

Sarah: They weren't silly. They were the things you believed in.

Maizie: Well I have better things to do with my time. *She folds the paper at the crossword puzzle and produces a pencil from a small, sensible looking purse.* Do any of you know a—let me see: three, four, five, six letter word for "something used in kitchen."

Sarah strongarms the other two away for a rapid fire conference.

Sarah: We've got to change her back to her old self.

Melody: Why?

Ivan: How?

Sarah: Run your machine backwards or something?

Melody: No.

Ivan: Backwards? You know so little about science, Sarah.

Melody: Why should we? She's perfectly normal. She's exactly what I had in mind.

Ivan: *Half to himself.* On the other hand, it might work. There's no harm in trying.

Sarah: *To Melody.* But she's given up all the things that made her special.

Melody: What's so bad about that?

Ivan: There are the exponential factors but . . .

Sarah: Do you really like her the way she is?

Ivan: Yeah! It might work!

Melody: *Stubborn but close to the breaking point.* Yes!

Ivan: *To the girls.* Hey!

Sarah: Why didn't you leave her the way she was? Why do you always try to change things?

Melody: *Exploding.* Because that's the way I am! *Pause.* That's the way I am. *Pause—and then Melody comes to a realization.* That's the thing that makes me special.

Sarah: Right!

Melody: But she was so strange!

Sarah: And so special.

Melody: Yeah.

Ivan: Maybe someday you'll find something that really needs changing.

Sarah: Right. And you'll change it.

Melody: Yeah, because that's the way I am, right?

Sarah: Right. But we shouldn't have started with Maizie.

Melody: *Looking towards Maizie again.* No. *Suddenly.* I shoulda started with you guys! You're the strange ones. *And she breaks away towards Maizie.*

Sarah and Ivan: Hey!

Melody: Maizie . . .

Maizie: *Still at the crossword puzzle.* "Blender", perhaps . . .

Melody: Maizie?

Maizie: Perhaps you should address me as Miss Maizie. One must show respect for one's elders, mustn't one?

Melody: Yes, Miss Maizie. Could you come with us?

Maizie: Where?

Melody: To Ivan's basement. We've found out there's a little change we have to make.

Maizie: No thank you.

Melody: *Coaxing.* Just a tiny wee change.

Maizie: I'd rather not.

Melody: You have to.

Maizie: Little girl, you must not tell a grown-up she has to do anything.

Melody: This calls for drastic action. *With that she snatches Maizie's purse and runs off with it—calling back to the others.* Hey you guys! Meet me at Ivan's house!

Maizie: Come back with that! Come back! I'll tell your mother!

Melody: *Struggling with herself.* Catch me if you can!

Maizie takes off after Melody and the other two run directly to Ivan's house, getting there before Melody arrives.

Scene 8: Ivan's Basement

Sarah: Get the machine ready!

Ivan: Right! Machine—are you ready? This time you've gotta work backwards! *To Sarah. As soon as Maizie is in the machine I'll turn it on.*

Sarah: Oh, I hope it works.

Ivan: It'd better!

Melody rushes in.

Melody: Quick! Start the machine!

Ivan: Where's Maizie?

Melody: I thought she was right behind me.

Sarah: Now what do we do?

Maizie staggers in, totally out of breath.

Maizie: *Gasping.* Give me that purse!

Melody: Sorry, Miss Maizie. You'll have to get it for yourself. *And she throws the purse into the machine.*

Maizie: You rude, inconsiderate, little brat! I'll teach you . . . *She is trying to reach the purse without going inside the machine.* I'll call the police, that's what I'll do. I'll have you sent away to reform school for purse snatching. See how you like that! And the rest of you are no better! Imagine treating an old lady like this. I'll have you reported. You are all in a lot of trouble, hear me? A lot of trouble. *But she is fully inside the machine—does the audience help to lure her inside?*

Melody and Sarah: Now! Now, Ivan!

Ivan: *Pulling the switch.* On!

Maizie: *Trying to get out.* Let me out of here!

Melody: In a minute, okay?

Maizie begins to feel the effects of the machine and then undergoes her earlier transformations in reverse order.

Melody: *Watching the changes.* Is that the one?

Sarah: No—not that one. That one. That's her!

Melody: That's right. Shut it down, Ivan!

Ivan: *Doing so.* Off!

Melody and Sarah escort Maizie out of the machine—Maizie is dazed, as before.

Melody: Maizie? *No response.*

Sarah: *Waving her hand over Maizie's eyes.* Yoohooo! *No response.*

Melody: *Shaking her gently.* Are you alright?

A huge smile spreads slowly across her face.

Maizie: Alright? Of course I am! I'm back to normal!

Ivan: Uh oh.

Melody: Normal?

Maizie catches sight of her bags and rushes to them like long lost friends. She produces a funny object like a collander and puts it on her head. She parades around in it.

Maizie: See? Normal!

Everybody congratulates her and one another. Suddenly Melody wails in anguish.

Maizie: What's wrong, Melody?

Melody: Our projects!

Sarah and Ivan: Our projects!

Maizie: What projects?

Ivan: Our school projects. Melody was supposed to change you into an ordinary sort of person and I was supposed to invent a habit remover and Sarah was supposed to tell a story.

Maizie: Well you've done all that . . .

Sarah: Not me.

Melody: And I haven't got anything to show for it anymore . . .

Ivan: And I don't think my machine is such a good idea anymore.

Maizie: Ah. *Pause.* Oh! *Getting everyone into a huddle.* Come on, I'll tell you what to do . . .

There is a lot of whispering and giggling. Then Maizie steps back and the children arrange themselves as if in the classroom.

Sarah: By doing this project, Miss Preedy, I learned that there are stories all around me. In fact I learned that there is one story going on all the time and that I am in it.

Ivan: By doing this project, Miss Preedy, I learned that sometimes I should always ask how my inventions should be used instead of just inventing them.

Melody: By doing this project, Miss Preedy, I learned that you should never take away the thing that makes a person special . . . Everybody is a little odd and there's nothing wrong with that.

Sarah: And here is how it all started: *Imitating Preedy.* "Class! Class!"

Ivan and Melody: Yes, Miss Preedy?

Sarah: "Have you all chosen your projects?"

Well, we could go on but you already know what happens. Everyone leaves, reciting lines from the beginning of the play.

■

V(A)ndal
William Horrocks

*Benjamin Darvill, Tracy Dahl, and Tom Anniko in the 1983
Prairie Theatre Exchange production.*

Vandal was the first produced by Project Prevention and
Prairie Theatre Exchange, Winnipeg, Manitoba on Tuesday,
April 5, 1983 with the following cast:

Phil ———————————————————————— Tom Anniko
Wendy ———————————————————————— Tracy Dahl
Mark ———————————————————————— Benjamin Darvill
Tod———————————————————————— Jeff Getty

Directed by Brian Richmond

Set and costume design: Gina-Aurea Widzinski
Lighting design: Clint DuVall
Original music: Bobby Stahr with lyrics by William Horrocks
and Brian Richmond

Requests for performance rights should be addressed to:

William Horrocks
Box 2732
Winnipeg, Manitoba
Canada

Information about the original music may be addressed to:

Bobby Stahr
23 Lenore Street
Winnipeg, Manitoba
Canada   R3G 2C1

The set is a long black wall angled from downstage to upstage with a long glass window at the upstage end. A ghetto blaster is sitting on a trunk centrestage and playing the preset music (an album by The Specials entitled Black and White.*) After the album is completed, a rent-a-cop in a clear face mask enters and changes the music tape. The Vandal theme comes up and the rent-a-cop exits. After the Vandal theme is completed, the lights go down and "ghosts", another musical number, is started. Wendy, carrying the ghetto blaster, Phil, dragging the trunk, and Tod enter, singing with the music. Mark jumps out of the trunk. All are wearing Hallowe'en masks. Tod is wearing a rubber face mask of someone (e.g. Yassar Arafat) currently held in the media to be diabolical. Wendy and Phil are wearing clear face masks. Mark is wearing a fly-face mask.*

Song: "Ghosts"

All: *Offstage.*
Ghosts, ghosts, ghosts, ghosts, ghosts,
Ghosts, ghosts, ghosts, ghosts, ghosts,
Ghosts, ghosts, ghosts, ghosts, ghosts,
Ghosts, ghosts, ghosts, ghosts, ghosts,

Phil: *Enters.* Snapping aerials.

Tod: *Enters.* Kicking dogs.

Mark: *Popping out of trunk.* Smashing glass.

Wendy: *Enters.* Scaring children.

All: Ghosts, ghosts, ghosts, ghosts
Ghosts, ghosts, ghosts, ghosts

Phil: Popping headlights.

Tod: Chasing cats.

Mark: Starting fires.

Wendy: Raising the dead.

Phil: Engineering frightful sights.

Tod: Chopping heads off little rats.

Mark: Cutting all the telephone wires.

Wendy: Breaking things on little heads.

Music fades repeating ghosts, actors exiting and lights fading.

This is the schoolyard after dark. The second week of October. A flashlight appears from behind the window and traces a path across the stage. This is obviously the rent-a-cop. A moment passes after the flashlight disappears and then a match flickers downstage to light a cigarette. A pause as the smoker takes a few lazy puffs and the cigarette glows in the dark. Then Wendy enters with the ghetto blaster playing her song.

Wendy:
To really place in life you need money.
Fill up my pockets with lots of money.
Don't really matter how you get it.
Long as you know the styles, you can spend it.

Chorus:
Calvin Klein
Will make you mine
Make, Make me, make me feel so fine.
Jordache jeans
What do they mean
They help me to make the scene.

I'm in the center of fashion passion
It costs a lot to buy new wave fashion.
I need to know I'm the main attraction.
I need money to stay in the action.

Repeat chorus.

Tod: Turn that thing off!

Wendy: What?

Tod: Turn it off!

Wendy: Oh. *Turns off machine.* Hi, Tod.

Tod: Wendy.

Wendy: What's up?

Tod: Keep the racket down.

Wendy: Just making conversation. Can I have a sip?

He passes her the bottle.

Wendy: Good Coke.

Tod: Will you keep your voice down.

Wendy: What's the matter with you, Tod? Getting paranoid?

Tod: Just sit quietly.

Wendy: You mean—the two of us? Alone in the dark?

Tod: Don't get fresh.

Wendy: Sorry Tod. Just trying to inject a little fun and humour into your drab little life.

Tod: Well, knock it off.

Wendy: Gimme another sip.

Tod: Some guy's wandering around with a flashlight.

Wendy: *Swallowing.* Cops?

Tod: I don't think so.

Wendy: Who do you think it is?

Tod: A rent-a-cop.

Wendy: In OUR schoolground?

Tod: Yeah.

Wendy: Who do they think they are?

Tod: Don't worry. We'll fix him.

Wendy: Maybe we should take off.

Tod: Chicken?

Wendy: You know I'm not, Tod.

Tod: Then take it easy. I told you, I've been watching him.

Wendy: Tod?

Tod: Yeah?

Wendy: Bum me a smoke.

Tod: Forget it.

Wendy: Just one.

Tod: I'm not running a charity.

Wendy: It won't kill ya.

Tod: What do I get in return?

Wendy: I'll pay you back tomorrow.

Tod: Where've I heard that before?

Wendy: Come on, Tod. One little cigarette.

Tod: What about the twenty bucks you owe me?

Wendy: You'll get it back.

Tod: Yeah? When? Tell you what, I'll give you a smoke but I want something in return.

Wendy: I told you before I'm not going to give you a back massage.

Tod: Do your geography?

Wendy: All twenty pages of it.

Tod: That's what I want. All twenty pages of it.

Wendy: For one cigarette?

Tod: You got it.

Wendy: But it took me three hours to finish. That's not a fair deal. Besides, Henderson'll see yours is the same as mine.

Tod: If you don't want a smoke—you don't want a smoke.

Wendy: Make it a pack and you got a deal.

Tod: Half a pack.

Wendy: Done.

He passes her cigarettes.

Tod: Ya see they painted the walls over again.

Wendy: Yeah. Too bad. There was some good stuff up.

Tod: There will be again.

Theme music starts. Tod spray paints "Fuzz Off" on the wall.

That rent-a-cop bugs me. You know why he's here, eh?

Wendy: To protect the school from little vandals.

Tod: Exactly. I guess he's gonna have to earn his pay.

Wendy: Right!

Tod: There he is!

Tod grabs ghetto blaster. They cross to exit. He turns machine way up.

Tod & Wendy: Hey!! Rent-a-cop!!

Flashlight scans the area. Tod and Wendy are gone. Flashlight settles on grafitti freshly written on wall. Darkness. The school bell rings. Lights up. Tod is leaning against wall looking bored. Wendy enters and attempts to sneak past him.

Tod: Wendy.

Wendy: Oh, good morning, Tod. How are you?

Tod: Hand it over.

Wendy: Hand what over?

Tod: I want your geography homework.

Wendy: Oh that. Why Tod, you should have said so in the first place. I know I have it in here somewheres.

Tod: I don't believe this. You gonna give it to me or not?

Wendy: There you go.

Tod: I'll copy it in Math class and give it back to you at lunch.

Wendy: Okay. But I'll need it for sure.

Tod: Don't worry about it. We got to talk to Phil about that rent-a-cop. After dark this is *our* schoolground and we aren't going to let them take it away from us.

Wendy: Exactly. So whatta we do?

Tod: I don't know. I'll think of something good.

Mark and Phil enter.

Phil: Inhuman superhuman master of disaster. Hi guys.

Tod: It walks. It talks. It's Phil the Pill.

Phil: Rock on into the sunset. Tod—Mark. Mark—Tod.

Mark: Hi.

Tod: Hiya, Red.

Mark: Name's Mark.

Tod: Red Mark. Mark the Narc.

Mark: Glad to meet ya, Tod—the clod—or is it sod or slob or maybe fraud.

Tod: Who is this kid, Phil?

Phil: New neighbours. Mark and his Old Man just moved in next door. Gonna be in our class too.

Tod: *To Wendy.* This midget in our class? School maybe—but he'll never be in our class.

Wendy: Hello.

Mark: Hi.

Tod: Guy's got a real way with words. So where were you last night?

Phil: With this new kid. Wanna hear what we did?

Tod: No.

Phil: We went back behind Higgins' place, you know. The guy left his car in neutral. And it's a bug, right. Real easy to push. So we push it all the way down the back lane and out into the street. We're going along and this car pulls up beside us. I figure this is it but Mark says—relax. Guy in the car rolls down his window, sticks out his head, and hollers—You boys need a hand? Mark here gives him this big smile and says—Sure! Next thing you know, the guy's out of his car and helping us push. What a riot. After he left, we rolled it onto the railroad tracks.

Tod: Big deal.

Phil: Whadda ya mean big deal?

Tod: That's nothing.

Phil: It was great!

Tod: *To Wendy.* Phil got a thrill.

Phil: At least, semi-great. Gimme a smoke.

Tod: Figure you rate one?

Phil: Always. *Tod passes him a cigarette.* What about Mark?

Tod: Smoke?

Mark: I don't smoke, thanks. *Pause.* Who needs lip cancer?

Tod: So who needs lips. Not you.

Mark: The only part of me that smokes is my feet.

Phil: Right on! This guy can really run, Tod.

Tod: Yeah? Well, I wanna see. You wanna hang out with us, kid, you gotta earn your membership.

Mark: How?

Tod: That's the fun part. *Removes Wendy's tape and replaces it with his own.* What is this "Dorothy and The Dreamwhips."

Phil: So what's up?

Tod: I don't like this kid.

Phil: He's new, Tod. You don't even know him.

Tod: I don't care! There's something about him I don't like!

Phil: Jeez, give him a break, will ya? What're ya getting so mad for?

Tod: Alright. I was gonna save this for Hallowe'en—but I think it would be the perfect initiation for Red there.

Phil: What's that, Tod?

Tod: Thompson's garden.

Phil: Alright!

Wendy: Clever, Tod, but there isn't much left in Thompson's garden this time of year.

Tod: Wrong, Little Red Riding Hood. Thompson's garden is full of soft gushy reject apples.

Phil/Wendy: Hallowe'en apples!

Tod: Mark here's going over the fence and after the ammunition.

Wendy: He's a new kid, Tod.

Tod: So what?

Phil: Yeah, don't worry, Wendy. Mark can handle it. Right Mark?

Mark: No sweat.

Phil: See?

Wendy: Better tell Mark about Spike.

Phil: Wendy!

Mark: Spike?

Wendy: Thompson's Doberman Pinscher.

Tod: The world's full of surprises, sport.

Mark: That sort of changes things.

Tod: Listen Red, why don't you take off eh? I think I hear your Mother calling. Shrimp!

Phil: You said you'd give the guy a chance, Tod.

Tod: Alright. How old are you?

Mark: What's that got to do with anything?

Tod: Ten? Eleven?

Mark: Thirteen!

Tod: Thirteen. When did you start babysitting, Phil . . .

Phil: Don't sweat it, Mark. Thompson's always got Spike on a leash.

Mark: How long a leash?

Tod: *Chuckles as he turns on ghetto blaster.* Look kid, first thing you gotta learn is not to ask stupid questions . . . You don't have control over the leash or anything else. It's all been decided— decided long before you ever came along.
Can't control my pimples, can't control my parents.
Can't control my sexual drive.
Can't control your red head hair, can't control your shortness,
Can't control your washed out eyes.

Chorus:
I'm running, I'm running, I'm running, I'm running from vacant eyes,
I'm running, I'm running, I'm running, I'm running,
I'm running from authorities' lies.

Vaccination, circumcision, Schools that run on cool precision,
Choices made before our time.
Evolution, revolution, things that give you brain pollution,
Decided all before our time.

Repeat chorus.

During musical break, Tod spray paints "V(A)NDAL" on glass window while Phil and Wendy write italicized words from the following verse on wall with chalk. Then they sing this verse.

Tod/Wendy/Phil:
Don't control the *bad dogs*
Don't control the *vandals*
Don't control the *beat*
Don't control the *back lane*
Don't control the *schoolyard*
Don't control the *street.*

Repeat chorus.

Tod: So you got it, kid. We're against things. Understand?

Mark: Yeah.

Tod: Good. Figure you got the guts to go over Thompson's fence?

Mark: Oh. Yeah.

Tod: We'll meet you back here after dark. Around nine thirty. Better wear your track shoes, Red—you're gonna need them. *Exits.*

Wendy: Wait up for me, Tod. *Exits.*

Mark: Phil, is there a pet store nearby?

Phil: Yeah. Adelman's. *Mark exits.* Hey Mark! What's your plan? *Phil exits.* Mark!!

It is after dark. The four enter. Phil and Wendy are loaded down with apples.

Wendy: Oh boy!

Phil: That was great!!

Wendy: I gotta catch my breath.

Phil: Me too. *A few moments pass as they do so.* Hey, Tod, whatta ya say now? Mark did okay.

Wendy: Phil's right. The kid really came across.

Phil: Yeah.

Wendy: Where'd he get that cage?

Phil: We got it. At Adelman's.

Wendy: What a great idea.

Phil: You ever see a cat look so scared before? *He starts to lob apples offstage.*

Wendy: Never. *She follows suit and also starts to lob apples offstage.*

Phil: And Spike?

Wendy: I'm sure he woulda killed that poor cat if he coulda got it out of the cage.

Phil: Hey, what's a matter with you guys? You passed with flying colours, Mark.

Mark: You told me that dog would be on a leash.

Phil: Well he *used* to be on a leash. But you got outa the yard okay, didn't ya?

Wendy: Where'd ya learn to run like that?

Phil: Yeah, I am really impressed with some of those moves you made tonight. What about you, Tod?

Wendy: Gotta admit it was pretty excellent stuff.

Tod: Doesn't take much to impress you two, does it?

Phil: The kid is *fast*, Tod.

Tod: So what. Let him go out for the track team.

Phil: We could use someone like that in the group. Hey, d'ya see that Wendy? I hit the stop sign.

Wendy: So what?

Phil: Bet you couldn't.

Wendy: Whadda ya wanna bet?

Phil: Your ghetto blaster for my new Adam Ant album.

Wendy: Get serious.

Phil: It's a good album.

Wendy: Not that good.

Phil: Okay, then a gentleman's bet.

Wendy: A gentleperson's bet.

Phil: Whatever. *Sticks his finger in his mouth and fakes puking.*

Tod: So what's the matter with you? Drop a load back there or something?

Mark: Being chased by a Doberman Pinscher is not my idea of a good time.

Tod: I thought it was pretty funny. Way you scrambled over that fence.

Mark: It *wasn't* funny! I coulda got killed!

Tod: You wouldn't a got killed.

Mark: How do you know?

Tod: I just know—alright.

Wendy: See! Told you I could hit it! D'you guys see that?

Tod: Yeah, yeah, we saw it.

Mark: That was a great shot, Wendy.

Tod: So who asked you?

Wendy: Thanks, Mark.

Mark: You don't like me much, do you?

Tod: Much! Try not at all.

Phil: Bet you can't hit the street light.

Wendy: Bet I can! There!! I hit it.

Phil: Yeah, big deal, anyone could do that. *Crosses to Tod.* Smoke? So what about Mark, Tod? Are you gonna let him in the gang?

Tod: Why are you so eager to let him in the gang?

Phil: You said if he did Thompson's garden, he could be in the gang.

Wendy: You did, Tod.

Tod: Alright, you guys win.

Phil: Hey!!

Wendy: Terrific!

Phil: Tod, that's great.

Tod: Sure.

Phil: Let's go stash this stuff somewhere until Hallowe'en. Then I'll walk you home.

Wendy: I want to wait for Tod. Tod, you coming?

Tod: In a while.

Wendy: Let's wait for him.

Phil: What for?

Wendy: I'd just like to—that's all.

Phil: I know what it is. You don't have to lie to me, Wendy.

Wendy: I'm not lying to you.

Phil: Yes, you are. Admit it—you don't trust yourself alone with me.

Wendy: What?

Phil: That's it, isn't it?

Wendy: What're you talking about?

Phil: You're afraid to be alone with me.

Wendy: Hardly.

Phil: You are. Because you won't be able to keep your hands off me.

Wendy: I don't believe this.

Phil: No, it's okay. Honest. I understand. I know how irresistible I am to women.

Wendy: Conceited or what.

Phil: We'd make a great looking couple.

Wendy: Sure. Me in my Calvin Klein's and you in the latest from Army Surplus. Tod, I can't carry my ghetto blaster with all this stuff.

Tod: Then leave it here. I'll drop it off at your house later.

Wendy: *Sighs.* Alright. Come on, Phil, let's go.

Phil: Catch you later.

Tod: Yeah.

Phil and Wendy exit. Mark and Tod are alone for the first time. Mark is about to exit. Tod blocks his path.

Tod: Thought you wanted to be in so bad?

Mark: I do.

Tod: Then why're you taking off?

Mark: The others are all gone.

Tod: Hey man, I'm the leader and I'm still here. You're some hotshot, aren't you? The way you sucked those other two in. So you're in for now. But we'll see just how long you last.

Mark: Hey, I can't help it if I'm short, Tod.

Tod: You're not just short! You're skinny, you're white, you wear glasses—and you're ugly. *Pause.* That's all we need, some puny little bone rack hanging around with us. Making us look bad.

Mark: I can't help the way I look. Why put me down like that?

Tod: Who's putting you down. I'm putting you in your place. So you run pretty fast.

Mark: Thanks.

Tod: For a shrimp. Why do you really wanna hang around with us anyway?

Mark: Gotta hang around somewhere. With someone. I like you guys. You're different. I mean who wants to hang around with the jerks and the jocks.

Tod: You do run pretty fast. And you're being small might come in handy. Who knows, you might be good for a laugh!

Mark: *Does* that mean I'm in?

Tod: I didn't say that. You're on probation. So what we gonna call ya?

Mark: Why d'ya hafta call me anything?

Tod: Gotta have a nickname like Phil the Pill. Or Trendy Wendy.

Mark: So what's your nickname?

Tod: Tod. Tod the God. Now lemme see—you're small, fast, can get into places. Firefly!! That's it. That's what I'll call ya. Firefly.

Mark: Firefly. That's kinda nice. They're bright. They're fast. Firefly, yeah, I like it.

Music

Mark:
Flies crawl up, they crawl up, they crawl up, crawl up schoolyard walls.
Flies go down, they go down, they go down, go down to see it all.
Flies go in, they go in, they go in, go in when no choice calls.
Flies can't be, they can't be, they can't be, can't be held in by walls.

Mark spray paints a fly on the wall.

Chorus:
Because they are the sons of the survivors.
They are sons of the survivors.

Flies have eyes, they have eyes, they have eyes, have eyes and see things a thousand ways.
Both eyes open, they're open, they're open, open every day.
One prank, two pranks, three pranks, four pranks, one prank that goes astray.
Flies have wings, they have wings, they have wings, have wings to fly away.

Tod: *Offers Mark sip of coke.* Where're you from, Firefly?

Mark: We move around a lot.

Tod: How come?

Mark: It's my Old Man. Works at different jobs. It's tough, you know. I mean, every school I go to everybody knows everybody else and I'm *always* the new kid. Soon as I get settled in a place and start to meet new people we have to move again.

Tod: Hey get down—GET DOWN. *Flashlight in window.* Jeez. That rent-a-cop is starting to get on my nerves. He's gone now.

Mark: Maybe he can't help it, Tod. Maybe it was all decided before *his* time too.

Tod: Yeah, maybe. Maybe, you're gonna be alright, Firefly. Well, it's getting late. See ya tomorrow.

Mark: Yeah. See ya tomorrow. Tod, thanks.

Lights down. School bell rings. Lights up on Tod in schoolyard. Wendy and Phil stride up to him.

Phil: Okay Tod, where is it?

Tod: Where's what?

Phil: Wendy's ghetto blaster.

Tod: Search me.

Phil: Don't tempt me.

Tod: Back off.

Wendy: I want it back, Tod.

Tod: Got the twenty bucks you owe me?

Wendy: No.

Tod: Well, unless you pay me back by tomorrow afternoon, I'm gonna have to sell your ghetto blaster.

Wendy: That's blackmail!

Tod: That's the world of high finance.

Phil: You know she's broke, Tod.

Tod: She's *always* broke! Spends all her money on designer jeans. Sweaters, make-up.

Wendy: It's called taste.

Tod: It's called stupid.

Wendy: I have to look good, Tod.

Tod: Well, you're gonna have to look good without your sound system. *Exits.*

Phil: What're you gonna do?

Wendy: I don't know.

Phil: Gotta find twenty bucks.

Wendy: Yeah, but where.

Phil: An advance on your allowance?

Wendy: Are you kidding? I already owe two years of allowance. I hafta practically beg to get lunch money these days.

Phil: Can you borrow it from someone?

Wendy: Sure. Then I owe somebody *else* twenty bucks.

Phil: But you'd have your ghetto blaster back.

Wendy: Got twenty bucks you can lend me, Phil?

Phil: Uh no, I—spent all my cash on albums this week.

Wendy: Sure. *Mark enters.* Mark!? We were just talking about you!

Mark: Oh?

Wendy: Yeah, sure we were. Right, Phil?

Phil: Yeah, what were we saying?

Wendy: I for one was really impressed with the moves you made last night.

Mark: Really?

Phil: Excellent stuff!

Mark: Thanks guys.

Wendy: Mark?

Mark: Yeah?

Wendy: Got twenty bucks you can lend me?

Phil: Boy, that was about as subtle as a brick.

Wendy: I really need it bad. I can pay you back Tuesday, for sure. Honest!

Mark: If I had twenty dollars I'd give it to ya—but I don't.

Wendy: So much for that idea.

Mark: What does she need it for?

Phil: Tod's gonna sell her ghetto blaster unless she pays him this money she owes him.

Wendy: What'm I gonna do? Wait a minute. I think I got it.

Phil: What?

Wendy: Last week I was in the teachers' staff room and they got a cigarette machine in there.

Phil: So?

Wendy: So at two-ten a pack, you wanna bet that machine is loaded with cash. Our problems are over. Woe!!

Phil: Hold it. What do you mean *our* problems are over? What's in it for us?

Wendy: You'll be my friend. Gonna help me, Mark?

Mark: Yeah. Sure.

Phil: Why?

Mark: Tod'll get his twenty bucks, Wendy her ghetto blaster, and me—

Wendy: A friend for life.

Mark: Sounds great.

Wendy: Gonna help, Phil?

Phil: I'll help ya. On one condition.

Wendy: What?

Phil: You and me. Saturday night. Roller skating.

Wendy: Gross me out. *Pause.*

Phil: Okay. *Starts to exit.*

Wendy: You can pick me up at seven thirty.

Phil: Alright! Now we just gotta figure out how we're gonna get into the staff room.

Mark: I got an idea.

Wendy: What?

Mark: Just before the lunch bell you can lock me in my locker.

Phil: What'll that do?

Mark: Every teacher in the school will be there trying to get in their two cents about the best way to get me out.

Phil: All they'll hafta do is go to the office and get your combination.

Mark: I'll use my bike lock—it has a key. I'll give it to Wendy just in case they can't get me out. She can—you know 'find it' if she has to.

Phil: So who's going in after the cigarette machine?

They are both looking at him.

Oh, now wait a minute.

Wendy: Come on, Phil.

Mark: If you're scared of being caught—

Phil: I'm not!

Mark: Then let's do it!

Phil: Alright Firefly, but this better work.

Mark: It'll work.

Phil: If it doesn't I'm gonna pound ya.

They exit. Blackout and then they re-enter on music. Wendy is carrying the ghetto blaster triumphantly. All three are quite excited.

Phil: *Song*
Hear the throbbing BEAT!
Sound of my running FEET
Hey, get out of my WAY
Hey, do as I SAY

Chorus:
'Cause I'm the inhuman superhuman master of disaster.
Thwacking throbbing thickhead, throbbing brickhead.
Master of disaster.

Repeat first verse.

Repeat chorus.

Wendy: I can't believe we actually pulled it off.

Phil: Yeah! Hey, this guy's pretty smart.

Wendy: You shoulda seen Henderson's face, Phil, when he found out how much the locksmith was gonna charge to get Mark out. He turned so white, I thought he was gonna just say the heck with it—leave the kid in there.

Phil: What'd they say when they got you out?

Mark: Nothing. I just played my sick role and they sent me to the nurse's room. Told them my back was turned and somebody came up, shoved me into the locker and then locked it.

Wendy: Boy, were they mad.

Phil: You were right about all the teachers taking off out of the staff room. It was weird being in there—'specially with no one else around.

Wendy: How much money's left?

Phil: Tons!

Mark: Alright.

Wendy: May as well split it up three ways.

Tod enters.

Mark: What about Tod?

Phil/Wendy: Good idea. You hang on to Tod's share, Mark.

Mark: Yeah, "Hey we got all this money. We broke into . . .

Tod pushes Mark violently against wall.

Phil: Hey, Tod. Come on.

Wendy: What're ya doing?

Phil: You're gonna hurt him.

Tod: Do you know who this sucker's Old Man is? That rent-a-cop that's been patrolling around the school.

Phil: What?

Wendy: You're kidding?

Tod: No, I'm not! This punk and his Old Man have been spying on us.

Wendy: Ya mean, we just broke into that cigarette machine with a RENT-A-COP'S kid!?

Phil: I'll kill him! Ya little—

Tod: Hold on, Phil, wait a minute.

Phil: I am gonna POUND—

Tod: Phil, I got a better idea.

Phil: What's that?

Tod: His Old Man's really been making it tough on us. Maybe Firefly here can help us solve the situation.

Wendy: What're you getting at, Tod?

Tod: Easy. We break into the school. Liberate a couple a tape decks or something and split.

Phil: So how does that get his Old Man?

Tod: If we break in and get away right under his nose, I think that'll be it for him—don't you? Listen Firefly, you're going in through the heating duct and then you're gonna let us in. How you take care of your Old Man and get him out of the way is your own business. You're gonna do this or I'll pull out your little creepy firefly eyes and squeeze them into your mother's orange juice.

Phil: But Tod, how do we know we can trust this guy? I mean, after the cigarette machine, he's got something on me.

Mark: *Quietly.* You can trust me.

Phil: Why should we believe you?

Mark: *Exploding.* YOU CAN TRUST ME!! *Going bananas.* How many times do I have to prove that to you guys!? YOU CAN TRUST ME! YOU CAN TRUST ME! You can trust me. Alright?

Tod: Tomorrow night.

Tod, Phil, and Wendy exit. Lights fade on Mark.

Wendy enters. She appears to be in shock. After a moment, Mark enters carrying lunch pail.

Wendy: *To herself.* I can't believe it.

Mark: Hey, Wendy.

Wendy: Mark.

Mark: What's a matter?

Wendy: Have you been inside the school yet?

Mark: Oh yeah.

Wendy: I just can't believe it.

Mark: I guess no classes today, eh?

Wendy: Or for the rest of the week.

Mark: *Gloating.* Too bad.

Wendy: The whole place's been wrecked!

Mark: I know.

Wendy: But who coulda done it.

Mark: Me.

Wendy: What?

Mark: I did it. It was me.

Wendy: *You* did all that damage inside the school?

Mark: Uh huh. Last night.

Wendy: You.

Mark: Pretty good, eh?

Wendy: *Why,* Mark?

Mark: I figured—why wait until tonight to do it. If I *really* wanted to prove to you guys that you could trust me, I would go in there by myself the night before and *do it.*

Wendy: Nobody was talking about wrecking half the school.

Mark: Well, I got in there, right, and it was the most fantastic feeling you could imagine. It was a snap getting in. I just slipped my Old Man a couple of sleeping pills in his coffee thermos and by the time I got through the heating duct he was out like a light. It was kinda strange at first—walking around inside with no lights on. Made me nervous. But then I started to get off on it. It was like a whole new world. No bells, teachers, or kids running through the halls.

Wendy: And so you went nuts.

Mark: Not right away, I was trying to figure out what to do when I saw I was right across from Henderson's office. And it came to me. Get Henderson. So I whipped this chair through the window and then sprayed shaving cream all over his papers, his files, inside all his desk drawers, and on the carpet.

Wendy: *Not impressed.* Sounds like fun.

Mark: It was great. Then I hit the gym locker and poured crazy glue in the jock straps? And the cafeteria, and the library! Oh, and the music room. I really cut loose in there. You'd be surprised how easy a violin can be snapped in two. And I wrecked the piano so it can't be played. Boy, I can imagine the look on their faces this morning.

Phil and Tod enter.

Phil: There he is!!

Tod: Phil, the cops are still watching. Hey! We wanna talk to you!!!

Mark: Hi!!! Did ya hear what I did!?

Phil: We heard.

Tod: You're gonna get it.

Mark: What's with you guys?

Tod: Don't play stupid with us.

Phil: Why'd you do it!?

Mark: I thought you'd be happy.

Tod: Yeah, sure.

Phil: We just spent the last hour in Henderson's office trying to tell the cops we didn't do it.

Mark: I never thought that would happen.

Tod: Then why'd you spray our symbol all over the walls!?

Mark: I wanted them to know it was us.

Phil: You stupid little . . .

Tod: Easy Phil.

Phil: It's a good thing we were both over at Wendy's last night with a bunch a people. Otherwise we'd be sitting in the cop shop right now!

Mark: You guys said you wanted me to prove myself.

Tod: You didn't prove *nothing!*

Mark: But I did!

Tod: All you proved was how much trouble you could cause us.

Phil: Yeah! Without *us* even having to be there!!

Mark: But I *did* go in there!

Tod: That was s'posed to be tonight!!

Mark: BUT I DID IT ANYWAYS!! BY MYSELF!!

Phil: Hey man, we weren't talking about destroying the school.

Tod: Just ripping off a couple of tape decks.

Mark: Ripping off a couple of tape decks. I thought you guys were tough.

Tod: Tough doesn't mean stupid.

Mark: You guys're always putting me down. For the way I look. For my Old Man. Everything I did, I did to prove I was okay.

Tod: I didn't like you the first time I saw you.

Mark: But last night I did something you guys only *talk* about doing.

Wendy: We do it for kicks, Mark. Not to hurt someone.

Mark: Yeah, right. Sneaking around after dark heaving apples at street lights and thinking you're hot stuff. Big deal.

Wendy: We just do it for fun.

Mark: You guys think you're better than me!

Tod: We are.

Mark: Some bigshots! Tod acting like some actor out of a movie and Wendy pretending she's a fashion model.

Phil: Don't try to leave the school grounds.

Mark: *To Phil.* You, ya put on your funny clothes and think that makes you special.

Phil: 'Cause when you do—

Mark: Well, it doesn't!

Phil: You're dead.

Mark: It makes you clowns in costumes! You're always playing these roles and talking about doing great things. You're not gonna do anything! I pity you.

Wendy: Why'd you have to wreck the school, Mark!?

Mark: BECAUSE IT WAS THERE! You guys aren't gonna touch me, you can't!! I'm the one with the guts!! You say they're watching us. Well, I don't care!

Throws lunch pail through window. The other three run off.

RUN! RUN! RUN! AND KEEP RUNNING!

Lights fade down somewhat. Mark puts on his fly mask and the others enter wearing their masks as at the beginning. To the music of "Ghosts" (part two) they bring on debris. It is vandalized property connected in some way to the media ghosts which haunt these children. Some objects are indicated. Each reader, actor and director can think of many more.

Phil: *Smashing remnants of broken window with his boot as he enters through it.* Bruce Lee. *Poster.*

Tod: The police. *Files.*

Mark: Parents.

Wendy: Marilyn Monroe. *Poster.*

Phil: Han Solo.

Tod: Marlon Brando. *Throws his leather jacket on the pile.*

Mark: Friendly Giant. *TV.*

Wendy: Dorothy and Toto. *Stuffed animal—dog.*

Phil: Dukes of Hazzard. *Car door.*

Tod: James Dean. *He rips off his James Dean T-shirt and throws it on the pile.*

Mark: Ronald McDonald.

Wendy: Jane Fonda.

Mark: Teachers.

Wendy: Calvin Klein. *Jeans.*

Tod rushes off and the others repeat a chorus of 'Tod' eight times. He re-enters draped in a Nazi flag and throws it on the pile.

Phil: Charlie Manson.

Tod: Mick Jagger. *Nazi flag.*

Mark: Mr. Rodgers.

Wendy: Pat Benetar.

Tod: Sid Vicious.

Mark: E. T. *Doll.*

Wendy: Cheryl Tiegs. *Fashion magazines.*

Phil: Wendy O. *Mannequin covered with shaving cream.*

Tod: Adam Ant. *Records and album covers.*

Mark: Big Bird.

Again Tod exits and the others sing a chorus of 'Tod' eight times. When he re-enters and starts to spray gasoline all over the huge pile of debris, they start from the beginning of this ghost sequence and, from opposite ends of the pile, ignite lighters. The lights fade as does the music and on the first repeat of 'Jane Fonda' the lights, the lighters, and the music wink out.

■

About the Editor

Joyce Doolittle has for many years been actively involved with drama for young people. She edited a special issue of *Canadian Theatre Review* (Spring, 1976) on Theatre for Young Audiences and was co-author, with Zina Barnieh, of *A Mirror of our Dreams: Children and Theatre in Canada* (Talonbooks, 1979). She was named honorary president of ASSITEJ CANADA, Association International du Théâtre pour l'Enfance et la Jeunesse, after a decade of representing Canada at international meetings. An Alberta Achievement Award in recognition of excellence in drama was awarded to her in 1978. In Calgary, Alberta, she founded the Pumphouse Theatre; one of the two performance spaces in this historic building will be dedicated in her name in September, 1984. Joyce Doolittle is frequently called upon to give papers on children's theatre and to conduct workshops in schools. She teaches Drama at the University of Calgary and remains active both as an actress and director.

Notes on Playwrights

■ **Edward Connell** was last seen playing *The Ragtime Kid* and acting as Music Director for Theatre Network's *The Shooting of Dan McGrew*. He has composed scores for the Citadel production of *King Lear* and the Northern Light/Phoenix production of *The Importance of Being Earnest*. He has provided music for everything from Shakespeare to *The Elephant Man*, including *The Other Side of the Pole*.

■ **Rex Deverell** was born in 1941 in Toronto and grew up in small-town Ontario. In 1971 he migrated west when his wife, Rita, was hired to perform in the Globe Theatre's Saskatchewan School Tour. Until then he had managed to pick up theological degrees in Hamilton, Ontario, and New York, N.Y., and had been a minister in St. Thomas, Ontario. He had also worked with an experimental theatre in Toronto.

The directors of the Globe, Ken and Sue Kramer, asked him to try his hand at writing for young people. After one false start he wrote a play called *Shortshrift* about the people in a little prairie town. That worked out well, and he followed it up with more plays about social issues for little tots. In 1975, the Globe took Rex on as Playwright-in-Residence, and he wrote a lot of plays for grown-ups—like *Boiler Room Suite, Drift, Righteousness,* and *Medicare!*. He liked writing those plays, but writing *Melody Meets the Bag Lady* seemed like coming back home.

■ **Marney Heatley** studied writing with Graeme Gibson and at the writers' colony at the Banff School of Fine Arts. In 1980, while studying children's literature at Carleton University, her play, *The Lion That Shouldn't Be*, toured Ottawa schools. She has also written for Sumwat Radio in Waterloo and won an award in the *Toronto Star* Short Story Contest. Marney is an avid Theatre Sports player and sometimes admits to being Stephen Heatley's sister. Her short story, *Meagan's Vampire*, has recently been published in *The Quarterly Journal*.

■ **Stephen Heatley** has been Artistic Director for Theatre Network for three seasons. During that time he has directed eight productions including the tours of *Rig, Pantages Presents, Country Choral,* and *The Other Side of the Pole.*

■ **William Horrocks** has been writing forever—but primarily from the age of eight when he discovered he couldn't paint. Horrocks, who claims to have prairie sunsets in his blood, maintains that Winnipeg, Manitoba is the center of the known universe. His chief writing influences have been Samuel Beckett, Harold Pinter, Tennessee Williams, John Fowles, Vladimir Nabokov, and Rod Sterling. William Horrocks received his early training in the radio and television course at Technical Vocational High School in Winnipeg. He was Playwright-in-Residence at Prairie Theatre Exchange for the 1982-83 season producing two scripts, *St. Peter's Asylum* for adults and *Vandal* for youth. He spent the summer of 1983 at the Banff School of Fine Arts as a member of the Playwrights' Colony. He is currently living in Thunder Bay working in association with Magus Theatre where he wrote *Teddy*, a children's Christmas show.

■ **W.O. Mitchell** is a legend in his own time. As a speaker and raconteur he is sought after and prized. His creation of memorable characters—many of them inhabitants of Crocus, Saskatchewan, the small town invented by the author to be the home of *Jake and the Kid*—is fecund in a Dickensian sense. He has written for many media. Among his well known and prize winning novels are *Who Has Seen the Wind, Vanishing Point*, and *How I Spent My Summer Holidays*. His successful stage plays, many of which had their first performances at Theatre Calgary, include *The Kite, Back to Beulah*, and *The Black Bonspiel of Willie MacCrimmon*. Plays which have been produced for young audiences, in addition to *The Day Jake Made Her Rain*, are *Cabin Fever* and *The Devil's Instrument*.

■ **Rick McNair** was born in Amherst, Nova Scotia, in 1941. Before coming to Theatre Calgary in 1977 to found and direct the Stage-Coach Players, he taught high school in Ontario for ten years. He is the author of over twenty plays for young people, including *Beowulf, Gulliver, Chagall, Napi The First Man, Merlin and Arthur*, and *Dr. Barnardo's Pioneers*.

In 1979 Rick McNair became Artistic Director of Theatre Calgary. New plays by Sharon Pollock and John Murrell and an adaptation of Robert Kroetsch's *Words of My Roaring* are testaments to McNair's commitment to works by living Canadian authors. Productions of W.O. Mitchell's plays, developed from other media, similarly attest to this priority. In April, 1984, he resigned from his post at Theatre Calgary and is now pursuing his interest in free-lance directing and writing.

■ **Brian Paisley** is the Artistic Director of Chinook Theatre. Born in Belfast and educated at the University of British Columbia, he has been writing, directing and teaching for fifteen years in England and Canada. He is the author of several plays for young people including *Tikta'liktak*, *The Odyssey*, *Blondin!*, *The Last White Christmas* and, with Robert Astle, *Clown A Round* and *Professor Arlecchino*. He is currently working on a new adaptation of the Sinbad legends. Brian is also the producer of Edmonton's annual Fringe Theatre Event, a highly successful festival of alternative and experimental productions.

■ **Alf Silver** was born in Brandon, Manitoba on Friday the 13th, 1951. He grew up in Grizwold, Manitoba, Winnipeg and Calgary. He studied Theatre and Broadcasting at Winnipeg's Technical and Vocational High School—before dropping out. His plays for young people produced by the Manitoba Theatre Workshop (now Prairie Theatre Exchange) include *More of a Family*, *Idiot Strings*, and *Saturday Night*. He has also written novels: *Good Time Charlie's Back In Town Again*, a French translation of *Good Time Charlie (Pas de quoi pleurer)*, and *A Savage Place*. Plays of Alf Silver produced at the Manitoba Theatre Centre while he was Playwright-in-Residence include *Thimblerig*, *Climate of the Times*, and *Clearances*. Alf Silver has worked as an actor, cab driver, laborer, cook, musician, guitar teacher, hospital TV rental agent . . .

■ When **Jan Truss** wrote her first play, she was still very close to her twenty-five-year career as a teacher. Hence, *Attack* had enough parts to keep any and every student in a high school class busy— and it was given second place in an Alberta Culture competition. Plays that followed, including *Cornelius Dragon*, were cut down to affordable, professional production size, requiring only four to six actors.

 Oomeraghi Oh!, a play for the very young, had its first performance in the Studio Theatre of the University of Calgary and went on to twenty-eight performances in Yugoslavia and six hundred as a marionette show in Quebec. *A Very Small Rebellion* and *The Judgement of Clifford Sifton* were developed and directed by Douglas Riske as part of the schools' program at Alberta Theatre Projects in Calgary.

 Coming to writing late, Jan Truss tried different forms: short stories for radio and magazines; poetry; a novel, *Bird At the Window*, which won the first Search for an Alberta Novelist Competition; a novel for children, *A Very Small Rebellion*, which is a

Children's Book Centre Choice; *Jasmin*, another novel chosen by children for the Ruth Schwartz Award, 1983.

All of Jan Truss's works are rooted in rural Alberta. She lives on a bushland farm in Water Valley with a view of the mountains. Currently she has an adult novel, *Etta Ryan*, with a publisher, and a young adult novel in the typewriter. *Silver City*, an opera for which she created the libretto, is in production.

■

Suggestions for Teaching

The plays in this collection are written by contemporary authors who live in the prairie provinces of Canada and together they cover diverse subjects in a variety of styles. For the casual reader they offer a unique look at the problems, hopes and dreams of young people. For producers, directors, and theatre companies this volume presents a choice of plays already tested on stage. Some ambitious teachers may find a script to produce here, but all teachers will discover material appropriate to enrich and enliven school work.

Language arts is the most obvious place to include study of these dramatic works. Reading a play can inspire student writing: characters in a play can be described in essay form, off-stage scenes can be invented, scenes occurring before the play begins and after its conclusion can be imagined and written as stories, poems or in script form. Discussions of character and plot development will increase the students' awareness of form, structure, and human personality. Talking or writing about how things might have changed had the characters behaved differently will help young people practise some of life's difficult decisions. Empathy with characters outside one's own life experience develops tolerance and compassion.

The plays can serve as inspiration for art, music and dance. Some students may wish to design stage settings and to construct a model set; others may be more interested in designing costumes. The rainmaking machine in *The Day Jake Made Her Rain* could be created by human bodies in a creative dance or drama exercise or designed and executed as an art project—or both. A group interested in puppetry can find scenes or an entire play in this collection for their project.

Tikta'liktak offers art opportunities in mask making and the opportunity to become a composer in developing a series of different drum beats for that omnipresent sound in the show. Creating a sound score for *Cornelius Dragon* challenges students to find and manufacture such diverse sounds as wind chimes, a deserted stretch of scorching summer prairie land and a tawdry circus, complete with a taped lion's roar. In devising the dances for *Vandal,* the students will be the experts—they know about contemporary popular dance styles.

Social studies and science classes can enlist aspects of various plays to broaden or illuminate their work. Plays like *Vandal, More of a Family*, and *Melody Meets the Bag Lady* present powerful proof of current social ills. A play like *Doctor Barnardo's Pioneers* can serve as the catalyst for an historical research project. A class can take a local historic event or a perceived local problem and can invent their own play from their findings, using the plays in this book as models of various styles through which they can tell their own story. *The Day Jake Made Her Rain* can be an ingredient in a study of weather's effects on man or on soils study. *Tikta'liktak* can inspire research study of Inuit peoples and the Canadian Arctic. Actually building a student designed rainmaking machine would call for mathematics skills and carpentry. A Christmas production of *The Other Side of the Pole* would demand the participation and cooperation of an entire school.

A play is like a blueprint—it must be read in a special way that requires active participation from the reader in imagining. A play is more sparse, distilled, and skeletal than fiction. The reader, the oral reader, the actor, the director, the designers: each must add his own imagination to the task at hand. The playwright provides a wealth of sensory stimuli and texture: sight, sound, sub-text; but we must fill in the specific shade, sound, action and reaction. Drama is a special form of thought—another language. Its study rewards the student with a broader understanding of his fellow man. ∎

Further Reading

Davis, Desmond. *Theatre for Young People.* Don Mills, Ontario: Musson Book Co., 1981.

Doolittle, Joyce, and Zina Barnieh. *A Mirror of Our Dreams— Children and the Theatre in Canada.* Vancouver: Talonbooks, 1979.

Doolittle, Joyce. "The Child: A Place in Life." *Canadian Theatre Review* 35 (Summer 1982): 50-66.

Wallace, Robert and Cynthia Zimmerman. *The Work: Conversations with English Canadian Playwrights.* Toronto: Coach House Press, 1982. On Rex Deverell, pp. 127-141.

Two Canadian magazines have published special issues on theatre for young audiences:

Canadian Theatre Review
Number 10   Spring 1976

Canadian Children's Literature
Double number 8 and 9   1977

For individual plays see publishers' catalogues, particularly Playwrights Canada, Simon and Pierre, and Talonbooks.